Illustrative
Mathematics®

Grade 7
Mathematics

UNIT

8

Student
Workbook

OPEN-UP
resources™

Contributors

Writing Team

Susan Addington

Ashli Black, Grade 8 Lead

Alicia Chiasson

Mimi Cukier

Nik Doran, Engineering Lead

Lisa England

Sadie Estrella

Kristin Gray

Donna Gustafson

Arias Hathaway

Bowen Kerins, Assessment Lead

Henry Kranendonk

Brigitte Lahme

Chuck Larrieu Casias

William McCallum, Shukongojin

Cam McLeman

Michelle Mourtgos, Grade 7 Lead

Mike Nakamaye

Kate Nowak, Instructional Lead

Roxy Peck, Statistics Lead

David Petersen

Sarah Pikcilingis

Liz Ramirez, Supports Lead

Lizzy Skousen

Yenche Tioanda, Grade 6 Lead

Kristin Umland, Content Lead

Supports for Students with Special Needs

Bridget Dunbar

Andrew Gael

Anthony Rodriguez

Supports for English Language Learners

Vinci Daro

Jack Dieckmann

James Malamut

Sara Rutherford-Quach

Renae Skarin

Steven Weiss

Jeff Zwiers

Digital Activities Development

Jed Butler

John Golden

Carrie Ott

Jen Silverman, Lead

Copy Editing

Emily Flanagan

Carolyn Hemmings

Tiana Hynes

Cathy Kessel, Lead

Nicole Lipitz

Robert Puchalik

Project Management

Aubrey Neihaus

Olivia Mitchell Russell, Lead

Engineering

Dan Blaker

Eric Connally

Jon Norstrom

Brendan Shean

Teacher Professional Learning

Vanessa Cerrahoglu

Craig Schneider

Jennifer Wilson

Alt Text

Donna Gustafson

Kia Johnson-Portee, Lead

Deb Barnum

Gretchen Hovan

Mary Cummins

Image Development

Josh Alves

Rob Chang

Rodney Cooke

Tiffany Davis

Jessica Haase

Christina Jackyra, Lead

Caroline Marks

Megan Phillips

Siavash Tehrani

Support Team

Madeleine Lowry

Nick Silverman

Melody Spencer

Alex Silverman

Hannah Winkler

Enhanced Print

Many activities have a QR code indicating that an interactive version of the activity is available online.

Just point your phone, tablet, or computer camera at the QR code and you'll be taken to the website version.

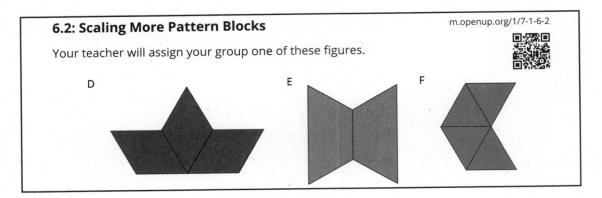

Don't have a QR reader on your device? Search the App Store or Google Play Store for a "QR reader."

Don't have a camera on your device? You can type in the web address above each code into a web browser.

Table of Contents

May 16th

Unit 8: Probability and Sampling

Lesson 1: Mystery Bags

Let's make predictions based on what we know.

1.1: Going Fishing

Andre and his dad have been fishing for 2 hours. In that time, they have caught 9 bluegills and 1 yellow perch.

The next time Andre gets a bite, what kind of fish do you think it will be? Explain your reasoning.

1.2: Playing the Block Game

Your teacher will give your group a bag of colored blocks.

1. Follow these instructions to play one round of the game:

   a. Everyone in the group records the color written on the bag in the first column of the table.
   b. Without looking in the bag, one person takes out one of the blocks and shows it to the group.
   c. If they get a block that is the same color as the bag, they earn:
      - 1 point during round 1
      - 2 points during round 2
      - 3 points during round 3

   d. Next, they put the block back into the bag, shake the bag to mix up the blocks, and pass the bag to the next person in the group.
   e. Repeat these steps until everyone in your group has had 4 turns.

2. At the end of the round, record each person's score in the table.

	What color bag?	person 1's score	person 2's score	person 3's score	person 4's score
round 1					
round 2					
round 3					

3. Pause here so your teacher can give you a new bag of blocks for the next round.

4. Repeat the previous steps to play rounds 2 and 3 of the game.

5. After you finish playing all 3 rounds, calculate the total score for each person in your group.

Are you ready for more?

Tyler's class played the block game using purple, orange, and yellow bags of blocks.

- During round 1, Tyler's group picked 4 purple blocks and 12 blocks of other colors.
- During round 2, Tyler's group picked 11 orange blocks and 5 blocks of other colors.
- During round 3, Tyler forgot to record how many yellow blocks his group picked.

For a final round, Tyler's group can pick one block from any of the three bags. Tyler's group decides that picking from the orange bag would give them the best chance of winning, and that picking from the purple bag would give them the worst chance of winning. What results from the yellow bag could have lead Tyler's group to this conclusion? Explain your reasoning.

Lesson 1 Summary

One of the main ways that humans learn is by repeating experiments and observing the results. Babies learn that dropping their cup makes it hit the floor with a loud noise by repeating this action over and over. Scientists learn about nature by observing the results of repeated experiments again and again. With enough data about the results of experiments, we can begin to predict what may happen if the experiment is repeated in the future. For example, a baseball player who has gotten a hit 33 out of 100 times at bat might be expected to get a hit about 33% of his times at bat in the future as well.

In some cases, we can predict the chances of things happening based on our knowledge of the situation. For example, a coin should land heads up about 50% of the time due to the symmetry of the coin.

In other cases, there are too many unknowns to predict the chances of things happening. For example, the chances of rain tomorrow are based on similar weather conditions we have observed in the past. In these situations, we can experiment, using past results to estimate chances.

Lesson 1 Practice Problems

1. Lin is interested in how many of her classmates watch her favorite TV show, so she starts asking around at lunch. She gets the following responses:

yes	yes	yes	no	no	no	no
no	no	no	yes	no	no	no

   If she asks one more person randomly in the cafeteria, do you think they will say "yes" or "no"? Explain your reasoning.

2. An engineer tests the strength of a new material by seeing how much weight it can hold before breaking. Previous tests have held these weights in pounds:

1,200	1,400	1,300	1,500	950	1,600	1,100

   Do you think that this material will be able to hold more than 1,000 pounds in the next test? Explain your reasoning.

3. A company tests two new products to make sure they last for more than a year. Product 1 had 950 out of 1,000 test items last for more than a year. Product 2 had 150 out of 200 last for more than a year. If you had to choose one of these two products to use for more than a year, which one is more likely to last? Explain your reasoning.

4. Put these numbers in order from least to greatest.

    a. $\frac{1}{2}$

    b. $\frac{1}{3}$

    c. $\frac{2}{5}$

    d. 0.6

    e. 0.3

5. A small staircase is made so that the horizontal piece of each step is 10 inches long and 25 inches wide. Each step is 5 inches above the previous one. What is the surface area of this staircase?

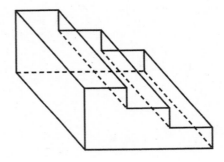

Lesson 2: Chance Experiments

Let's investigate chance.

2.1: Which is More Likely?

Which is more likely to happen?

1. When reaching into a dark closet and pulling out one shoe from a pile of 20 pairs of shoes, you pull out a left shoe.

2. When listening to a playlist—which has 5 songs on it—in shuffle mode, the first song on the playlist plays first.

2.2: How Likely Is It?

1. Label each **event** with one of these options:

> impossible,   unlikely,   equally likely as not,   likely,   certain

a. You will win grand prize in a raffle if you purchased 2 out of the 100 tickets.

b. You will wait less than 10 minutes before ordering at a fast food restaurant.

c. You will get an even number when you roll a standard number cube. *Unlikely*

d. A four-year-old child is over 6 feet tall. *Certain*

e. No one in your class will be late to class next week.

f. The next baby born at a hospital will be a boy.

g. It will snow at our school on July 1.

h. The sun will set today before 11:00 p.m.

i. Spinning this spinner will result in green.

j. Spinning this spinner will result in yellow.

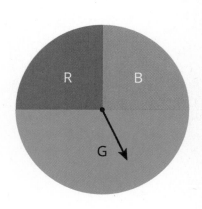

2. Discuss your answers to the previous question with your partner. If you disagree, work to reach an agreement.

3. Invent another situation for each label, for a total of 5 more events.

2.3: Take a Chance

m.openup.org/1/7-8-2-3

Your teacher will have 2 students play a short game.

1. When the first person chose 3 numbers, did they usually win?

2. When the person chose 4 numbers, did you expect them to win? Why?

Are you ready for more?

On a game show, there are 3 closed doors. One door has a prize behind it. The contestant chooses one of the doors. The host of the game show, who knows where the prize is located, opens one of the *other* doors which does not have the prize. The contestant can choose to stay with their first choice or switch to the remaining closed door.

1. Do you think it matters if the contestant switches doors or stays?

2. Practice playing the game with your partner and record your results. Whoever is the host starts each round by secretly deciding which door has the prize.
   a. Play 20 rounds where the contestant always stays with their first choice.
   b. Play 20 more rounds where the contestant always switches doors.

3. Did the results from playing the game change your answer to the first question? Explain.

2.4: Card Sort: Likelihood

1. Your teacher will give you some cards that describe events. Order the events from least likely to most likely.

2. After ordering the first set of cards, pause here so your teacher can review your work. Then, your teacher will give you a second set of cards.

3. Add the new set of cards to the first set so that all of the cards are ordered from least likely to most likely.

Lesson 2 Summary

A **chance experiment** is something that happens where the outcome is unknown. For example, if we flip a coin, we don't know if the result will be a head or a tail. An **outcome** of a chance experiment is something that can happen when you do a chance experiment. For example, when you flip a coin, one possible outcome is that you will get a head. An **event** is a set of one or more outcomes.

We can describe events using these phrases:

- Impossible
- Unlikely
- Equally likely as not
- Likely
- Certain

For example, if you flip a coin:

- It is *impossible* that the coin will turn into a bottle of ketchup.
- It is *unlikely* the coin will land on its edge.
- It is *equally likely as not* that you will get a tail.
- It is *likely* that you will get a head or a tail.
- It is *certain* that the coin will land somewhere.

The *probability* of an event is a measure of the likelihood that an event will occur. We will learn more about probabilities in the lessons to come.

Lesson 2 Glossary Terms

- event
- outcome
- chance experiment

Lesson 2 Practice Problems

1. The likelihood that Han makes a free throw in basketball is 60%. The likelihood that he makes a 3-point shot is 0.345. Which event is more likely, Han making a free throw or making a 3-point shot? Explain your reasoning.

2. Different events have the following likelihoods. Sort them from least to greatest:

   a. 60%

   b. 8 out of 10

   c. 0.37

   d. 20%

   e. $\frac{5}{6}$

3. There are 25 prime numbers between 1 and 100. There are 46 prime numbers between 1 and 200. Which is more likely? Explain your reasoning.

   a. A computer produces a random number between 1 and 100 that is prime.

   b. A computer produces a random number between 1 and 200 that is prime.

4. It takes $4\frac{3}{8}$ cups of cheese, $\frac{7}{8}$ cups of olives, and $2\frac{5}{8}$ cups of sausage to make a signature pizza. How much of each ingredient is needed to make 10 pizzas? Explain or show your reasoning.

5.

Here is a diagram of a birdhouse Elena is planning to build. (It is a simplified diagram, since in reality, the sides will have a thickness.) About how many square inches of wood does she need to build this birdhouse?

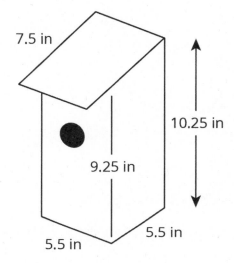

7.5 in

10.25 in

9.25 in

5.5 in

5.5 in

6. Select **all** the situations where knowing the surface area of an object would be more useful than knowing its volume.

    A. Placing an order for tiles to replace the roof of a house.
    B. Estimating how long it will take to clean the windows of a greenhouse.
    C. Deciding whether leftover soup will fit in a container.
    D. Estimating how long it will take to fill a swimming pool with a garden hose.
    E. Calculating how much paper is needed to manufacture candy bar wrappers.
    F. Buying fabric to sew a couch cover.
    G. Deciding whether one muffin pan is enough to bake a muffin recipe.

Lesson 3: What Are Probabilities?

Let's find out what's possible.

3.1: Which Game Would You Choose?

Which game would you choose to play? Explain your reasoning.

Game 1: You flip a coin and win if it lands showing heads.

Game 2: You roll a standard number cube and win if it lands showing a number that is divisible by 3.

3.2: What's Possible?

1. For each situation, list the **sample space** and tell how many outcomes there are.

    a. Han rolls a standard number cube once.

    b. Clare spins this spinner once.

    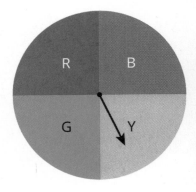

    c. Kiran selects a letter at **random** from the word "MATH."

d. Mai selects a letter at random from the alphabet.

e. Noah picks a card at random from a stack that has cards numbered 5 through 20.

2. Next, compare the likelihood of these outcomes. Be prepared to explain your reasoning.

   a. Is Clare more likely to have the spinner stop on the red or blue section?

   b. Is Kiran or Mai more likely to get the letter T?

   c. Is Han or Noah more likely to get a number that is greater than 5?

3. Suppose you have a spinner that is evenly divided showing all the days of the week. You also have a bag of papers that list the months of the year. Are you more likely to spin the current day of the week or pull out the paper with the current month?

Are you ready for more?

Are there any outcomes for two people in this activity that have the same likelihood? Explain or show your reasoning.

3.3: What's in the Bag?

Your teacher will give your group a bag of paper slips with something printed on them. Repeat these steps until everyone in your group has had a turn.

- As a group, guess what is printed on the papers in the bag and record your guess in the table.
- Without looking in the bag, one person takes out one of the papers and shows it to the group.
- Everyone in the group records what is printed on the paper.
- The person who took out the paper puts it back into the bag, shakes the bag to mix up the papers, and passes the bag to the next person in the group.

	Guess the sample space.	What is printed on the paper?
person 1		
person 2		
person 3		
person 4		

1. How was guessing the sample space the fourth time different from the first?

2. What could you do to get a better guess of the sample space?

3. Look at all the papers in the bag. Were any of your guesses correct?

4. Are all of the possible outcomes equally likely? Explain.

5. Use the sample space to determine the **probability** that a fifth person would get the same outcome as person 1.

Lesson 3 Summary

The **probability** of an event is a measure of the likelihood that the event will occur. Probabilities are expressed using numbers from 0 to 1.

If the probability is 0, that means the event is impossible. For example, when you flip a coin, the probability that it will turn into a bottle of ketchup is 0. The closer the probability of some event is to 0, the less likely it is.

If the probability is 1, that means the event is certain. For example, when you flip a coin, the probability that it will land somewhere is 1. The closer the probability of some event is to 1, the more likely it is.

If we list all of the possible outcomes for a chance experiment, we get the **sample space** for that experiment. For example, the sample space for rolling a standard number cube includes six outcomes: 1, 2, 3, 4, 5, and 6. The probability that the number cube will land showing the number 4 is $\frac{1}{6}$. In general, if all outcomes in an experiment are equally likely and there are n possible outcomes, then the probability of a single outcome is $\frac{1}{n}$.

Sometimes we have a set of possible outcomes and we want one of them to be selected at **random**. That means that we want to select an outcome in a way that each of the outcomes is *equally likely*. For example, if two people both want to read the same book, we could flip a coin to see who gets to read the book first.

Lesson 3 Glossary Terms

- random
- sample space
- probability

Lesson 3 Practice Problems

1. List the *sample space* for each chance experiment.

    a. Flipping a coin

    b. Selecting a random season of the year

    c. Selecting a random day of the week

2. A computer randomly selects a letter from the alphabet.

    a. How many different outcomes are in the sample space?

    b. What is the probability the computer produces the first letter of your first name?

3. What is the probability of selecting a random month of the year and getting a month that starts with the letter "J?" If you get stuck, consider listing the sample space.

4. E represents an object's weight on Earth and M represents that same object's weight on the Moon. The equation $M = \frac{1}{6}E$ represents the relationship between these quantities.

    a. What does the $\frac{1}{6}$ represent in this situation?

    b. Give an example of what a person might weigh on Earth and on the Moon.

5.

Here is a diagram of the base of a bird feeder which is in the shape of a pentagonal prism. Each small square on the grid is 1 square inch.

The distance between the two bases is 8 inches. What will be the volume of the completed bird feeder?

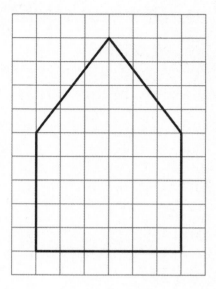

6. Find the surface area of the triangular prism.

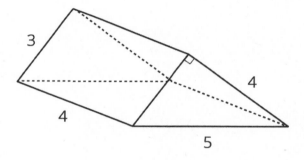

Lesson 4: Estimating Probabilities Through Repeated Experiments

Let's do some experimenting.

4.1: Decimals on the Number Line

1. Locate and label these numbers on the number line.

   a. 0.5
   b. 0.75
   c. 0.33
   d. 0.67
   e. 0.25

2. Choose one of the numbers from the previous question. Describe a game in which that number represents your probability of winning.

4.2: In the Long Run

m.openup.org/1/7-8-4-2

Mai plays a game in which she only wins if she rolls a 1 or a 2 with a standard number cube.

1. List the outcomes in the sample space for rolling the number cube.

2. What is the probability Mai will win the game? Explain your reasoning.

Grade 7
Mathematics

3. If Mai is given the option to flip a coin and win if it comes up heads, is that a better option for her to win?

4. With your group, follow these instructions 10 times to create the graph.

   ○ One person rolls the number cube. Everyone records the outcome.
   ○ Calculate the fraction of rolls that are a win for Mai so far. Approximate the fraction with a decimal value rounded to the hundredths place. Record both the fraction and the decimal in the last column of the table.
   ○ On the graph, plot the number of rolls and the fraction that were wins.
   ○ Pass the number cube to the next person in the group.

roll	outcome	total number of wins for Mai	fraction of games played that are wins
1			
2			
3			
4			
5			
6			
7			
8			
9			
10			

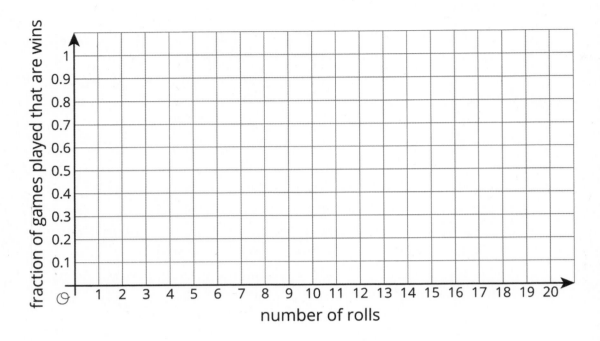

5. What appears to be happening with the points on the graph?

6.   a. After 10 rolls, what fraction of the total rolls were a win?

     b. How close is this fraction to the probability that Mai will win?

7. Roll the number cube 10 more times. Records your results in this table and on the graph from earlier.

roll	outcome	total number of wins for Mai	fraction of games played that are wins
11			
12			
13			
14			
15			
16			
17			
18			
19			
20			

8.   a. After 20 rolls, what fraction of the total rolls were a win?

    b. How close is this fraction to the probability that Mai will win?

4.3: Due For a Win

1. For each situation, do you think the result is surprising or not? Is it possible? Be prepared to explain your reasoning.

    a. You flip the coin once, and it lands heads up.

    b. You flip the coin twice, and it lands heads up both times.

    c. You flip the coin 100 times, and it lands heads up all 100 times.

2. If you flip the coin 100 times, how many times would you expect the coin to land heads up? Explain your reasoning.

3. If you flip the coin 100 times, what are some other results that would not be surprising?

4. You've flipped the coin 3 times, and it has come up heads once. The cumulative fraction of heads is currently $\frac{1}{3}$. If you flip the coin one more time, will it land heads up to make the cumulative fraction $\frac{2}{4}$?

Lesson 4 Summary

A probability for an event represents the proportion of the time we expect that event to occur in the long run. For example, the probability of a coin landing heads up after a flip is $\frac{1}{2}$, which means that if we flip a coin many times, we expect that it will land heads up about half of the time.

Even though the probability tells us what we should expect if we flip a coin many times, that doesn't mean we are more likely to get heads if we just got three tails in a row. The chances of getting heads are the same every time we flip the coin, no matter what the outcome was for past flips.

Lesson 4 Practice Problems

1. A carnival game has 160 rubber ducks floating in a pool. The person playing the game takes out one duck and looks at it.

   ○ If there's a red mark on the bottom of the duck, the person wins a small prize.
   ○ If there's a blue mark on the bottom of the duck, the person wins a large prize.
   ○ Many ducks do not have a mark.

   After 50 people have played the game, only 3 of them have won a small prize, and none of them have won a large prize.

   Estimate the number of the 160 ducks that you think have red marks on the bottom. Then estimate the number of ducks you think have blue marks. Explain your reasoning.

2. Lin wants to know if flipping a quarter really does have a probability of $\frac{1}{2}$ of landing heads up, so she flips a quarter 10 times. It lands heads up 3 times and tails up 7 times. Has she proven that the probability is not $\frac{1}{2}$? Explain your reasoning.

3. A spinner is spun 40 times for a game. Here is a graph showing the fraction of games that are wins under some conditions.

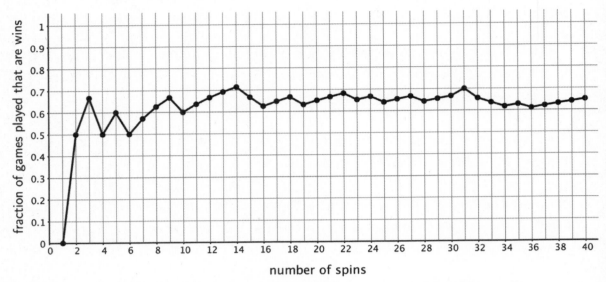

Estimate the probability of a spin winning this game based on the graph.

4. Which event is more likely: rolling a standard number cube and getting an even number, or flipping a coin and having it land heads up?

5. Noah will select a letter at random from the word "FLUTE." Lin will select a letter at random from the word "CLARINET."

   Which person is more likely to pick the letter "E?" Explain your reasoning.

Lesson 5: More Estimating Probabilities

Let's estimate some probabilities.

5.1: Is it Likely?

1. If the weather forecast calls for a 20% chance of light rain tomorrow, would you say that it is likely to rain tomorrow?

2. If the probability of a tornado today is $\frac{1}{10}$, would you say that there will likely be a tornado today?

3. If the probability of snow this week is 0.85, would you say that it is likely to snow this week?

5.2: Making My Head Spin

m.openup.org/1/7-8-5-2

Your teacher will give you 4 spinners. Make sure each person in your group uses a different spinner.

1. Spin your spinner 10 times, and record your outcomes.

2. Did you get all of the different possible outcomes in your 10 spins?

3. What fraction of your 10 spins landed on 3?

4. Next, share your outcomes with your group, and record their outcomes.

    a. Outcomes for spinner A:

    b. Outcomes for spinner B:

    c. Outcomes for spinner C:

    d. Outcomes for spinner D:

5. Do any of the spinners have the same sample space? If so, do they have the same probabilities for each number to result?

6. For each spinner, what is the probability that it lands on the number 3? Explain or show your reasoning.

7. For each spinner, what is the probability that it lands on something other than the number 3? Explain or show your reasoning.

8. Noah put spinner D on top of his closed binder and spun it 10 times. It never landed on the number 1. How might you explain why this happened?

9. Han put spinner C on the floor and spun it 10 times. It never landed on the number 3, so he says that the probability of getting a 3 is 0. How might you explain why this happened?

Are you ready for more?

Design a spinner that has a $\frac{2}{3}$ probability of landing on the number 3. Explain how you could precisely draw this spinner.

5.3: How Much Green?

Your teacher will give you a bag of blocks that are different colors. Do not look into the bag or take out more than 1 block at a time. Repeat these steps until everyone in your group has had 4 turns.

- Take one block out of the bag and record whether or not it is green.
- Put the block back into the bag, and shake the bag to mix up the blocks.
- Pass the bag to the next person in the group.

1. What do you think is the probability of taking out a green block from this bag? Explain or show your reasoning.

2. How could you get a better estimate without opening the bag?

Lesson 5 Summary

Suppose a bag contains 5 blocks. If we select a block at random from the bag, then the probability of getting any one of the blocks is $\frac{1}{5}$.

Now suppose a bag contains 5 blocks. Some of the blocks have a star, and some have a moon. If we select a block from the bag, then we will either get a star block or a moon block. The probability of getting a star block depends on how many there are in the bag.

In this example, the probability of selecting a star block at random from the first bag is $\frac{1}{5}$, because it contains only 1 star block. (The probability of getting a moon block is $\frac{4}{5}$.) The probability of selecting a star block at random from the second bag is $\frac{3}{5}$, because it contains 3 star blocks. (The probability of getting a moon block from this bag is $\frac{2}{5}$.)

This shows that two experiments can have the same sample space, but different probabilities for each outcome.

Lesson 5 Practice Problems

1. What is the same about these two experiments? What is different?

   - Selecting a letter at random from the word "ALABAMA"
   - Selecting a letter at random from the word "LAMB"

2. Andre picks blocks out of a bag 60 times and notes that 43 of them were green.

   a. What should Andre estimate for the probability of picking out a green block from this bag?

   b. Mai looks in the bag and sees that there are 6 blocks in the bag. Should Andre change his estimate based on this information? If so, what should the new estimate be? If not, explain your reasoning.

3. A person suspects that a standard number cube is not so standard. He rolls it 100 times, and it lands on a six 40 times. Another person rolls this cube 100 times, and it lands on a six 42 times. A third person rolls the cube 100 times, and it lands on a six 33 times. Based on the results, is there evidence to help prove that this cube is not a standard number cube? Explain your reasoning.

4. A textbook has 428 pages numbered in order starting with 1. You flip to a random page in the book in a way that it is equally likely to stop at any of the pages.

    a. What is the sample space for this experiment?

    b. What is the probability that you turn to page 45?

    c. What is the probability that you turn to an even numbered page?

5. A rectangular prism is cut along a diagonal on each face to create two triangular prisms. The distance between A and B is 5 inches.

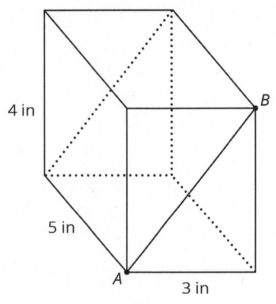

What is the surface area of the original rectangular prism? What is the total surface area of the two triangular prisms together?

Grade 7
Mathematics

Lesson 6: Estimating Probabilities Using Simulation

Let's simulate real-world situations.

6.1: Which One Doesn't Belong: Spinners

Which spinner doesn't belong?

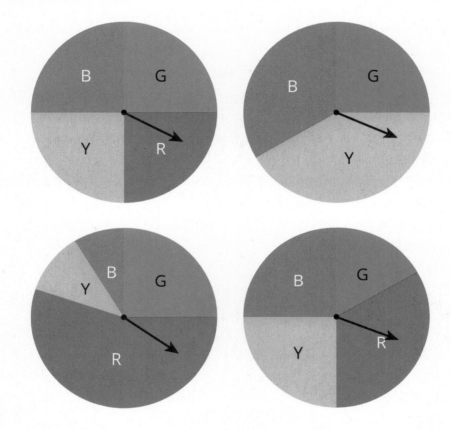

6.2: Diego's Walk

Your teacher will give your group the supplies for one of the three different simulations. Follow these instructions to simulate 15 days of Diego's walk. The first 3 days have been done for you.

- Simulate one day:
  - If your group gets a bag of papers, reach into the bag, and select one paper without looking inside.
  - If your group gets a spinner, spin the spinner, and see where it stops.
  - If your group gets two number cubes, roll both cubes, and add the numbers that land face up. A sum of 2–8 means Diego has to wait.

- Record in the table whether or not Diego had to wait more than 1 minute.
- Calculate the total number of days and the cumulative fraction of days that Diego has had to wait so far.
- On the graph, plot the number of days and the fraction that Diego has had to wait. Connect each point by a line.
- If your group has the bag of papers, put the paper back into the bag, and shake the bag to mix up the papers.
- Pass the supplies to the next person in the group.

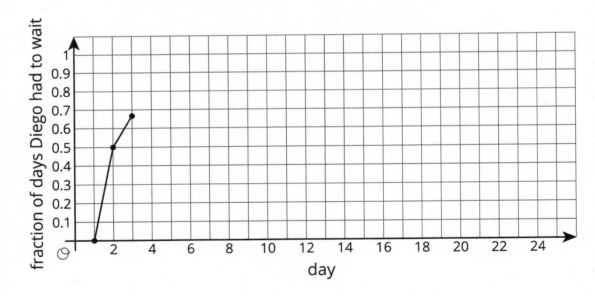

day	Does Diego have to wait more than 1 minute?	total number of days Diego had to wait	fraction of days Diego had to wait
1	no	0	$\frac{0}{1} = 0.00$
2	yes	1	$\frac{1}{2} = 0.50$
3	yes	2	$\frac{2}{3} \approx 0.67$
4			
5			
6			
7			
8			
9			
10			
11			
12			
13			
14			
15			

1. Based on the data you have collected, do you think the fraction of days Diego has to wait after the 16th day will be closer to 0.9 or 0.7? Explain or show your reasoning.

2. Continue the simulation for 10 more days. Record your results in this table and on the graph from earlier.

day	Does Diego have to wait more than 1 minute?	total number of days Diego had to wait	fraction of days Diego had to wait
16			
17			
18			
19			
20			
21			
22			
23			
24			
25			

3. What do you notice about the graph?

4. Based on the graph, estimate the probability that Diego will have to wait more than 1 minute to cross the crosswalk.

Are you ready for more?

Let's look at why the values tend to not change much after doing the simulation many times.

1. After doing the simulation 4 times, a group finds that Diego had to wait 3 times. What is an estimate for the probability Diego has to wait based on these results?

   a. If this group does the simulation 1 more time, what are the two possible outcomes for the fifth simulation?

   b. For each possibility, estimate the probability Diego has to wait.

   c. What are the differences between the possible estimates after 5 simulations and the estimate after 4 simulations?

2. After doing the simulation 20 times, this group finds that Diego had to wait 15 times. What is an estimate for the probability Diego has to wait based on these results?

   a. If this group does the simulation 1 more time, what are the two possible outcomes for the twenty-first simulation?

   b. For each possibility, estimate the probability Diego has to wait.

   c. What are the differences between the possible estimates after 21 simulations and the estimate after 20 simulations?

3. Use these results to explain why a single result after many simulations does not affect the estimate as much as a single result after only a few simulations.

6.3: Designing Experiments

For each situation, describe a chance experiment that would fairly represent it.

1. Six people are going out to lunch together. One of them will be selected at random to choose which restaurant to go to. Who gets to choose?

2. After a robot stands up, it is equally likely to step forward with its left foot or its right foot. Which foot will it use for its first step?

3. In a computer game, there are three tunnels. Each time the level loads, the computer randomly selects one of the tunnels to lead to the castle. Which tunnel is it?

4. Your school is taking 4 buses of students on a field trip. Will you be assigned to the same bus that your math teacher is riding on?

Lesson 6 Summary

Sometimes it is easier to estimate a probability by doing a *simulation*. A simulation is an experiment that approximates a situation in the real world. Simulations are useful when it is hard or time-consuming to gather enough information to estimate the probability of some event.

For example, imagine Andre has to transfer from one bus to another on the way to his music lesson. Most of the time he makes the transfer just fine, but sometimes the first bus is late and he misses the second bus. We could set up a simulation with slips of paper in a bag. Each paper is marked with a time when the first bus arrives at the transfer point. We select slips at random from the bag. After many trials, we calculate the fraction of the times that he missed the bus to estimate the probability that he will miss the bus on a given day.

Lesson 6 Practice Problems

1. The weather forecast says there is a 75% chance that it will rain later today.

    a. Draw a spinner that you could use to simulate this probability.

    b. Describe another way you could simulate this probability.

2. An experiment will produce one of ten different outcomes with equal probability for each. Why would using a standard number cube to simulate the experiment be a bad choice?

3. An ice cream shop offers 40 different flavors. To simulate the most commonly chosen flavor, you could write the name of each flavor on a piece of paper and put it in a bag. Draw from the bag 100 times, and see which flavor is chosen the most. Why is this simulation a bad way to figure out the most commonly chosen flavor?

4. Each set of three numbers represents the lengths, in units, of the sides of a triangle. Which set can *not* be used to make a triangle?

    A. 7, 6, 14

    B. 4, 4, 4

    C. 6, 6, 2

    D. 7, 8,13

5. There is a proportional relationship between a volume measured in cups and the same volume measured in tablespoons. 48 tablespoons is equivalent to 3 cups, as shown in the graph.

   a. Plot and label some more points that represent the relationship.

   b. Use a straightedge to draw a line that represents this proportional relationship.

   c. For which value y is $(1, y)$ on the line you just drew?

   d. What is the constant of proportionality for this relationship?

   e. Write an equation representing this relationship. Use c for cups and t for tablespoons.

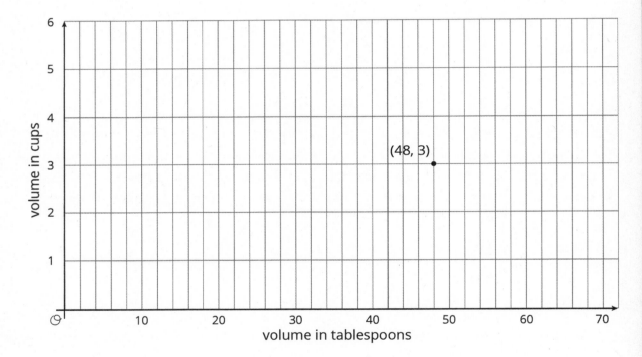

Lesson 7: Simulating Multi-step Experiments

Let's simulate more complicated events.

7.1: Ski Business

What do you notice? What do you wonder?

7.2: Alpine Zoom

m.openup.org/1/7-8-7-2

Alpine Zoom is a ski business. To make money over spring break, they need it to snow at least 4 out of the 10 days. The weather forecast says there is a $\frac{1}{3}$ chance it will snow each day during the break.

1. Describe a chance experiment that you could use to simulate whether it will snow on the first day of spring break.

2. How could this chance experiment be used to determine whether Alpine Zoom will make money?

Pause here so your teacher can give you the supplies for a simulation.

3. Simulate the weather for 10 days to see if Alpine Zoom will make money over spring break. Record your results in the first row of the table.

	day 1	day 2	day 3	day 4	day 5	day 6	day 7	day 8	day 9	day 10	Did they make money?
simulation 1											
simulation 2											
simulation 3											
simulation 4											
simulation 5											

4. Repeat the previous step 4 more times. Record your results in the other rows of the table.

5. Based on your group's simulations, estimate the probability that Alpine Zoom will make money.

7.3: Kiran's Game

Kiran invents a game that uses a board with alternating black and white squares. A playing piece starts on a white square and must advance 4 squares to the other side of the board within 5 turns to win the game.

For each turn, the player draws a block from a bag containing 2 black blocks and 2 white blocks. If the block color matches the color of the next square on the board, the playing piece moves onto it. If it does not match, the playing piece stays on its current square.

1. Take turns playing the game until each person in your group has played the game twice.

2. Use the results from all the games your group played to estimate the probability of winning Kiran's game.

3. Do you think your estimate of the probability of winning is a good estimate? How could it be improved?

Are you ready for more?

How would each of these changes, on its own, affect the probability of winning the game?

1. Change the rules so that the playing piece must move 7 spaces within 8 moves.

2. Change the board so that all the spaces are black.

3. Change the blocks in the bag to 3 black blocks and 1 white block.

7.4: Simulation Nation

Match each situation to a simulation.

Situations:

A. In a small lake, 25% of the fish are female. You capture a fish, record whether it is male or female, and toss the fish back into the lake. If you repeat this process 5 times, what is the probability that at least 3 of the 5 fish are female?

B. Elena makes about 80% of her free throws. Based on her past successes with free throws, what is the probability that she will make exactly 4 out of 5 free throws in her next basketball game?

C. On a game show, a contestant must pick one of three doors. In the first round, the winning door has a vacation. In the second round, the winning door has a car. What is the probability of winning a vacation and a car?

D. Your choir is singing in 4 concerts. You and one of your classmates both learned the solo. Before each concert, there is an equal chance the choir director will select you or the other student to sing the solo. What is the probability that you will be selected to sing the solo in exactly 3 of the 4 concerts?

Simulations:

1. Toss a standard number cube 2 times and record the outcomes. Repeat this process many times and find the proportion of the simulations in which a 1 or 2 appeared both times to estimate the probability.

2. Make a spinner with four equal sections labeled 1, 2, 3, and 4. Spin the spinner 5 times and record the outcomes. Repeat this process many times and find the proportion of the simulations in which a 4 appears 3 or more times to estimate the probability.

3. Toss a fair coin 4 times and record the outcomes. Repeat this process many times, and find the proportion of the simulations in which exactly 3 heads appear to estimate the probability.

4. Place 8 blue chips and 2 red chips in a bag. Shake the bag, select a chip, record its color, and then return the chip to the bag. Repeat the process 4 more times to obtain a simulated outcome. Then repeat this process many times and find the proportion of the simulations in which exactly 4 blues are selected to estimate the probability.

Lesson 7 Summary

The more complex a situation is, the harder it can be to estimate the probability of a particular event happening. Well-designed simulations are a way to estimate a probability in a complex situation, especially when it would be difficult or impossible to determine the probability from reasoning alone.

To design a good simulation, we need to know something about the situation. For example, if we want to estimate the probability that it will rain every day for the next three days, we could look up the weather forecast for the next three days. Here is a table showing a weather forecast:

	today (Tuesday)	Wednesday	Thursday	Friday
probability of rain	0.2	0.4	0.5	0.9

We can set up a simulation to estimate the probability of rain each day with three bags.

- In the first bag, we put 4 slips of paper that say "rain" and 6 that say "no rain."

- In the second bag, we put 5 slips of paper that say "rain" and 5 that say "no rain."

- In the third bag, we put 9 slips of paper that say "rain" and 1 that says "no rain."

Then we can select one slip of paper from each bag and record whether or not there was rain on all three days. If we repeat this experiment many times, we can estimate the probability that there will be rain on all three days by dividing the number of times all three slips said "rain" by the total number of times we performed the simulation.

Lesson 7 Practice Problems

1. Priya's cat is pregnant with a litter of 5 kittens. Each kitten has a 30% chance of being chocolate brown. Priya wants to know the probability that at least two of the kittens will be chocolate brown.

To simulate this, Priya put 3 white cubes and 7 green cubes in a bag. For each trial, Priya pulled out and returned a cube 5 times. Priya conducted 12 trials. Here is a table with the results.

trial number	outcome
1	ggggg
2	gggwg
3	wgwgw
4	gwggg
5	gggwg
6	wwggg
7	gwggg
8	ggwgw
9	wwwgg
10	ggggw
11	wggwg
12	gggwg

a. How many successful trials were there? Describe how you determined if a trial was a success.

b. Based on this simulation, estimate the probability that *exactly* two kittens will be chocolate brown.

c. Based on this simulation, estimate the probability that *at least* two kittens will be chocolate brown.

d. Write and answer another question Priya could answer using this simulation.

e. How could Priya increase the accuracy of the simulation?

Grade 7
Mathematics

2. A team has a 75% chance to win each of the 3 games they will play this week. Clare simulates the week of games by putting 4 pieces of paper in a bag, 3 labeled "win" and 1 labeled "lose." She draws a paper, writes down the result, then replaces the paper and repeats the process two more times. Clare gets the result: win, win, lose. What can Clare do to estimate the probability the team will win at least 2 games?

3.   a. List the sample space for selecting a letter a random from the word "PINEAPPLE."

    b. A letter is randomly selected from the word "PINEAPPLE." Which is more likely, selecting "E" or selecting "P?" Explain your reasoning.

4. On a graph of side length of a square vs. its perimeter, a few points are plotted.

    a. Add at least two more ordered pairs to the table and the graph.

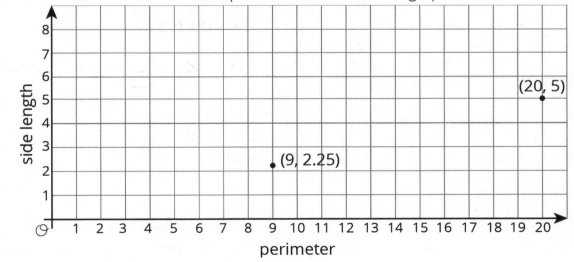

    b. Is there a proportional relationship between the perimeter and side length? Explain how you know.

Lesson 8: Keeping Track of All Possible Outcomes

Let's explore sample spaces for experiments with multiple parts.

8.1: How Many Different Meals?

How many different meals are possible if each meal includes one main course, one side dish, and one drink?

[handwritten: 06 breadsticks, Coffee, Fizzy]

main courses	side dishes	drinks
grilled chicken	salad	milk
turkey sandwich	applesauce	juice
pasta salad		water

[handwritten: Pizza 3 × 2 × 3, 18 meals, 4 × 3 × 5 = 60]

8.2: Lists, Tables, and Trees

Consider the experiment: Flip a coin, and then roll a number cube.

Elena, Kiran, and Priya each use a different method for finding the sample space of this experiment.

- Elena carefully writes a list of all the options: Heads 1, Heads 2, Heads 3, Heads 4, Heads 5, Heads 6, Tails 1, Tails 2, Tails 3, Tails 4, Tails 5, Tails 6

- Kiran makes a table:

	1	2	3	4	5	6
H	H1	H2	H3	H4	H5	H6
T	T1	T2	T3	T4	T5	T6

- Priya draws a tree with branches where each pathway represents a different outcome:

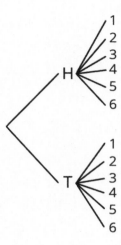

1. Compare the three methods. What is the same about each method? What is different? Be prepared to explain why each method produces all the different outcomes without repeating any.

2. Which method do you prefer for this situation?

Pause here so your teacher can review your work.

3. Find the sample space for each of these experiments using any method. Make sure you list every possible outcome without repeating any.

    a. Flip a dime, then flip a nickel, and then flip a penny. Record whether each lands heads or tails up.

    b. Han's closet has: a blue shirt, a gray shirt, a white shirt, blue pants, khaki pants, and black pants. He must select one shirt and one pair of pants to wear for the day.

    c. Spin a color, and then spin a number.

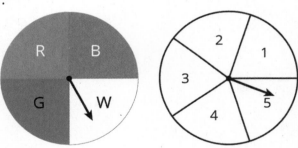

    d. Spin the hour hand on an analog clock, and then choose AM or PM.

STOP

Grade 7
Mathematics

8.3: How Many Sandwiches?

1. A submarine sandwich shop makes sandwiches with one kind of bread, one protein, one choice of cheese, and two vegetables. How many different sandwiches are possible? Explain your reasoning. You do not need to write out the sample space.

   - Breads: Italian, White, Wheat
   - Proteins: Tuna, Ham, Turkey, Beans
   - Cheese: Provolone, Swiss, American, None
   - Vegetables: Lettuce, Tomatoes, Peppers, Onions, Pickles

   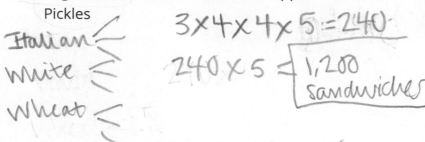

   Italian
   White
   Wheat

   $3 \times 4 \times 4 \times 5 = 240$

   $240 \times 5 = \boxed{1,200 \text{ sandwiches}}$

2. Andre knows that he wants a sandwich that has ham, lettuce, and tomatoes on it. He doesn't care about the type of bread or cheese. How many of the different sandwiches would make Andre happy?

   $1 \times 3 \times 4 \times 1 \times 1 = \boxed{12 \text{ sandwiches}}$

3. If a sandwich is made by randomly choosing each of the options, what is the probability that it will be a sandwich that Andre would be happy with?

   $\dfrac{12}{1,200} = \boxed{1\% \text{ chance}}$

Are you ready for more?

Describe a situation that involves three parts and has a total of 24 outcomes in the sample space.

- letter to parents
- 1 on 1 w/ students
- see what students want to focus on

Lesson 8 Summary

Sometimes we need a systematic way to count the number of outcomes that are possible in a given situation. For example, suppose there are 3 people (A, B, and C) who want to run for the president of a club and 4 different people (1, 2, 3, and 4) who want to run for vice president of the club. We can use a *tree*, a *table*, or an *ordered list* to count how many different combinations are possible for a president to be paired with a vice president.

With a tree, we can start with a branch for each of the people who want to be president. Then for each possible president, we add a branch for each possible vice president, for a total of $3 \cdot 4 = 12$ possible pairs. We can also start by counting vice presidents first and then adding a branch for each possible president, for a total of $3 \cdot 4 = 12$ possible pairs.

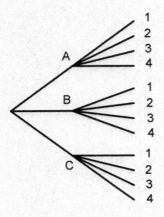 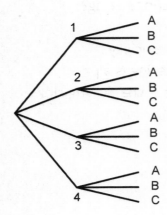

A table can show the same result:

	1	2	3	4
A	A, 1	A, 2	A, 3	A, 4
B	B, 1	B, 2	B, 3	B, 4
C	C, 1	C, 2	C, 3	C, 4

So does this ordered list:

A1, A2, A3, A4, B1, B2, B3, B4, C1, C2, C3, C4

Lesson 8 Practice Problems

1. Noah is planning his birthday party. Here is a tree showing all of the possible themes, locations, and days of the week that Noah is considering.

   a. How many themes is Noah considering? *3*

   b. How many locations is Noah considering? *2*

   c. How many days of the week is Noah considering? *3*

   d. One possibility that Noah is considering is a party with a space theme at the skating rink on Sunday. Write two other possible parties Noah is considering.

   • safari at the park on friday
   • comics at the skating rink on Saturday

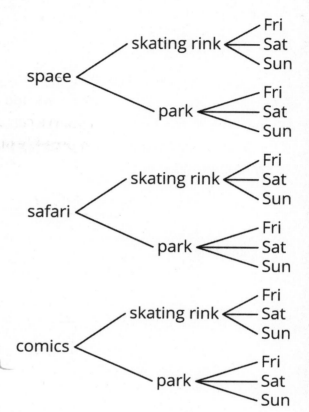

   e. How many different possible outcomes are in the sample space?

   3×2×3 = 18 possible

2. For each event, write the sample space and tell how many outcomes there are.

   a. Lin selects one type of lettuce and one dressing to make a salad.

   - Lettuce types: iceberg, romaine
   - Dressings: ranch, Italian, French

   b. Diego chooses rock, paper, or scissors, and Jada chooses rock, paper, or scissors.

c. Spin these 3 spinners.

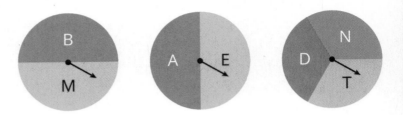

3. A simulation is done to represent kicking 5 field goals in a single game with a 72% probability of making each one. A 1 represents making the kick and a 0 represents missing the kick.

trial	result
1	10101
2	11010
3	00011
4	11111
5	10011

Based on these results, estimate the probability that 3 or more kicks are made.

4. There is a bag of 50 marbles.

- Andre takes out a marble, records its color, and puts it back in. In 4 trials, he gets a green marble 1 time.
- Jada takes out a marble, records its color, and puts it back in. In 12 trials, she gets a green marble 5 times.
- Noah takes out a marble, records its color, and puts it back in. In 9 trials, he gets a green marble 3 times.

Estimate the probability of getting a green marble from this bag. Explain your reasoning.

Lesson 9: Multi-step Experiments

Let's look at probabilities of experiments that have multiple steps.

9.1: True or False?

Is each equation true or false? Explain your reasoning.

$8 = (8 + 8 + 8 + 8) \div 3$

$(10 + 10 + 10 + 10 + 10) \div 5 = 10$

$(6 + 4 + 6 + 4 + 6 + 4) \div 6 = 5$

9.2: Spinning a Color and Number

The other day you wrote the sample space for spinning each of these spinners once.

What is the probability of getting:

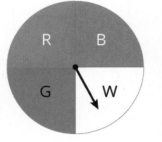
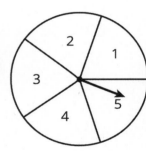

1. green and 3?

2. blue and any odd number?

3. any color other than red and any number other than 2?

9.3: Cubes and Coins

The other day you looked at a list, a table, and a tree that showed the sample space for rolling a number cube and flipping a coin.

1. Your teacher will assign you one of these three structures to use to answer these questions. Be prepared to explain your reasoning.

    a. What is the probability of getting tails and a 6?

    b. What is the probability of getting heads and an odd number?

    Pause here so your teacher can review your work.

2. Suppose you roll two number cubes. What is the probability of getting:

    a. both cubes showing the same number?

    b. *exactly* one cube showing an even number?

    c. *at least* one cube showing an even number?

    d. two values that have a sum of 8?

    e. two values that have a sum of 13?

3. Jada flips three quarters. What is the probability that all three will land showing the same side?

9.4: Pick a Card

Imagine there are 5 cards. They are colored red, yellow, green, white, and black. You mix up the cards and select one of them without looking. Then, without putting that card back, you mix up the remaining cards and select another one.

1. Write the sample space and tell how many possible outcomes there are.

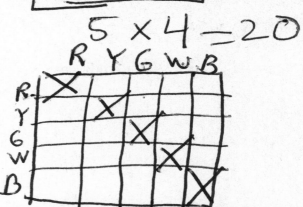

2. What structure did you use to write all of the outcomes (list, table, tree, something else)? Explain why you chose that structure.

3. What is the probability that:

   a. you get a white card and a red card (in either order)?

   b. you get a black card (either time)?

   c. you do not get a black card (either time)?

   d. you get a blue card?

   e. you get 2 cards of the same color?

   f. you get 2 cards of different colors?

Are you ready for more?

In a game using five cards numbered 1, 2, 3, 4, and 5, you take two cards and add the values together. If the sum is 8, you win. Would you rather pick a card and put it back before picking the second card or keep the card in your hand while you pick the second card? Explain your reasoning.

Lesson 9 Summary

Suppose we have two bags. One contains 1 star block and 4 moon blocks. The other contains 3 star blocks and 1 moon block.

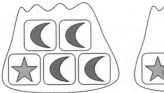

If we select one block at random from each, what is the probability that we will get two star blocks or two moon blocks?

To answer this question, we can draw a tree diagram to see all of the possible outcomes.

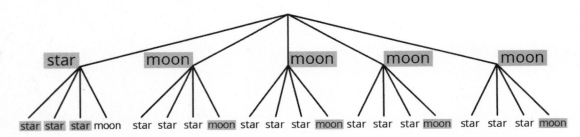

There are $5 \cdot 4 = 20$ possible outcomes. Of these, 3 of them are both stars, and 4 are both moons. So the probability of getting 2 star blocks or 2 moon blocks is $\frac{7}{20}$.

In general, if all outcomes in an experiment are equally likely, then the probability of an event is the fraction of outcomes in the sample space for which the event occurs.

Lesson 9 Practice Problems

1. A vending machine has 5 colors (white, red, green, blue, and yellow) of gumballs and an equal chance of dispensing each. A second machine has 4 different animal-shaped rubber bands (lion, elephant, horse, and alligator) and an equal chance of dispensing each. If you buy one item from each machine, what is the probability of getting a yellow gumball and a lion band?

2. The numbers 1 through 10 are put in one bag, and the numbers 5 through 14 are put in another bag. When you pick one number from each bag, what is the probability you get the same number?

3. When rolling 3 standard number cubes, the probability of getting all three numbers to match is $\frac{6}{216}$. What is the probability that the three numbers *do not* all match? Explain your reasoning.

4. For each event, write the sample space and tell how many outcomes there are.

   a. Roll a standard number cube. Then, flip a quarter.

   b. Select a month. Then, select 2020 or 2025.

5. On a graph of the area of a square vs. its perimeter, a few points are plotted.

   a. Add some more ordered pairs to the table and graph.

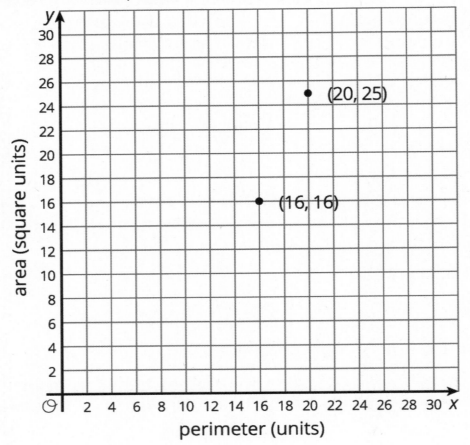

   b. Is there a proportional relationship between the area and perimeter of a square? Explain how you know.

Lesson 10: Designing Simulations

Let's simulate some real-life scenarios.

10.1: Number Talk: Division

Find the value of each expression mentally.

$(4.2 + 3) \div 2$

$(4.2 + 2.6 + 4) \div 3$

$(4.2 + 2.6 + 4 + 3.6) \div 4$

$(4.2 + 2.6 + 4 + 3.6 + 3.6) \div 5$

10.2: Breeding Mice

m.openup.org/1/7-8-10-2

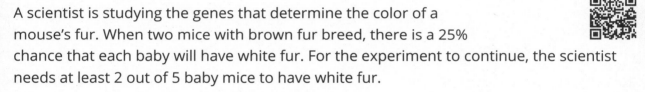

A scientist is studying the genes that determine the color of a mouse's fur. When two mice with brown fur breed, there is a 25% chance that each baby will have white fur. For the experiment to continue, the scientist needs at least 2 out of 5 baby mice to have white fur.

To simulate this situation, you can flip a coin twice for each baby mouse.

- If the coin lands heads up both times, it represents a mouse with white fur.
- Any other result represents a mouse with brown fur.

1. Simulate 3 litters of 5 baby mice and record your results in the table.

	mouse 1	mouse 2	mouse 3	mouse 4	mouse 5	Do at least 2 have white fur?
simulation 1						
simulation 2						
simulation 3						

2. Based on the results from everyone in your group, estimate the probability that the scientist's experiment will be able to continue.

3. How could you improve your estimate?

Are you ready for more?

For a certain pair of mice, the genetics show that each offspring has a probability of $\frac{1}{16}$ that they will be albino. Describe a simulation you could use that would estimate the probability that at least 2 of the 5 offspring are albino.

10.3: Designing Simulations

Your teacher will give your group a paper describing a situation.

1. Design a simulation that you could use to estimate a probability. Show your thinking. Organize it so it can be followed by others.

2. Explain how you used the simulation to answer the questions posed in the situation.

Lesson 10 Summary

Many real-world situations are difficult to repeat enough times to get an estimate for a probability. If we can find probabilities for parts of the situation, we may be able to simulate the situation using a process that is easier to repeat.

For example, if we know that each egg of a fish in a science experiment has a 13% chance of having a mutation, how many eggs do we need to collect to make sure we have 10 mutated eggs? If getting these eggs is difficult or expensive, it might be helpful to have an idea about how many eggs we need before trying to collect them.

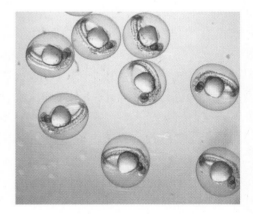

We could simulate this situation by having a computer select random numbers between 1 and 100. If the number is between 1 and 13, it counts as a mutated egg. Any other number would represent a normal egg. This matches the 13% chance of each fish egg having a mutation.

We could continue asking the computer for random numbers until we get 10 numbers that are between 1 and 13. How many times we asked the computer for a random number would give us an estimate of the number of fish eggs we would need to collect.

To improve the estimate, this entire process should be repeated many times. Because computers can perform simulations quickly, we could simulate the situation 1,000 times or more.

Lesson 10 Practice Problems

1. A rare and delicate plant will only produce flowers from 10% of the seeds planted. To see if it is worth planting 5 seeds to see any flowers, the situation is going to be simulated. Which of these options is the best simulation? For the others, explain why it is not a good simulation.

   a. Another plant can be genetically modified to produce flowers 10% of the time. Plant 30 groups of 5 seeds each and wait 6 months for the plants to grow and count the fraction of groups that produce flowers.

   b. Roll a standard number cube 5 times. Each time a 6 appears, it represents a plant producing flowers. Repeat this process 30 times and count the fraction of times at least one number 6 appears.

   c. Have a computer produce 5 random digits (0 through 9). If a 9 appears in the list of digits, it represents a plant producing flowers. Repeat this process 300 times and count the fraction of times at least one number 9 appears.

   d. Create a spinner with 10 equal sections and mark one of them "flowers." Spin the spinner 5 times to represent the 5 seeds. Repeat this process 30 times and count the fraction of times that at least 1 "flower" was spun.

2. The figure on the left is a trapezoidal prism. The figure on the right represents its base. Find the volume of this prism.

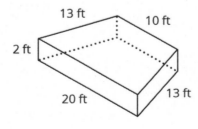
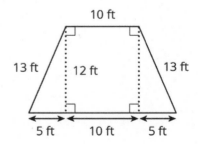

3. Jada and Elena learned that 8% of students have asthma. They want to know the probability that in a team of 4 students, at least one of them has asthma. To simulate this, they put 25 slips of paper in a bag. Two of the slips say "asthma." Next, they take four papers out of the bag and record whether at least one of them says "asthma." They repeat this process 15 times.

- Jada says they could improve the accuracy of their simulation by using 100 slips of paper and marking 8 of them.
- Elena says they could improve the accuracy of their simulation by conducting 30 trials instead of 15.

a. Do you agree with either of them? Explain your reasoning.

b. Describe another method of simulating the same scenario.

4. Match each expression in the first list with an equivalent expression from the second list.

A. $(8x + 6y) + (2x + 4y)$　　　　　　　　1. $10(x + y)$

B. $(8x + 6y) - (2x + 4y)$　　　　　　　　2. $10(x - y)$

C. $(8x + 6y) - (2x - 4y)$　　　　　　　　3. $6(x - \frac{1}{3}y)$

D. $8x - 6y + 2x + 4y$　　　　　　　　　4. $8x + 6y + 2x - 4y$

E. $8x - 6y + 2x - 4y$　　　　　　　　　5. $8x + 6y - 2x + 4y$

F. $8x - (-6y - 2x + 4y)$　　　　　　　　6. $8x - 2x + 6y - 4y$

Lesson 11: Comparing Groups

Let's compare two groups.

11.1: Notice and Wonder: Comparing Heights

What do you notice? What do you wonder?

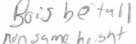

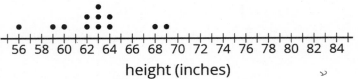

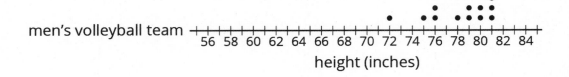

11.2: More Team Heights

1. How much taller is the volleyball team than the gymnastics team?

   ○ Gymnastics team's heights (in inches) : 56, 59, 60, 62, 62, 63, 63, 63, 64, 64, 68, 69

   ○ Volleyball team's heights (in inches): 72, 75, 76, 76, 78, 79, 79, 80, 80, 81, 81, 81

63   81

2. Make dot plots to compare the heights of the tennis and badminton teams.

   ○ Tennis team's heights (in inches): 66, 67, 69, 70, 71, 73, 73, 74, 75, 75, 76

   ○ Badminton team's heights (in inches): 62, 62, 65, 66, 68, 71, 73

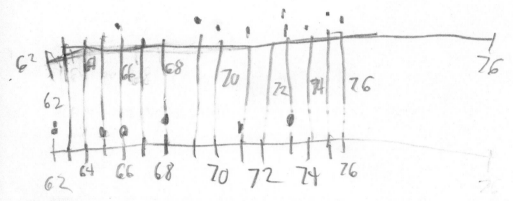

   What do you notice about your dot pots?

3. Elena says the members of the tennis team were taller than the badminton team. Lin disagrees. Do you agree with either of them? Explain or show your reasoning.

11.3: Family Heights

Compare the heights of these two families. Explain or show your reasoning.

- The heights (in inches) of Noah's family members: 28, 39, 41, 52, 63, 66, 71

- The heights (in inches) of Jada's family members: 49, 60, 68, 70, 71, 73, 77

Are you ready for more?

If Jada's family adopts newborn twins who are each 18 inches tall, does this change your thinking? Explain your reasoning.

11.4: Track Length

Here are three dot plots that represent the lengths, in minutes, of songs on different albums.

A

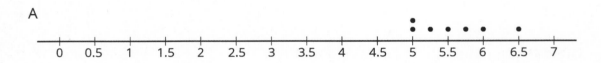

B

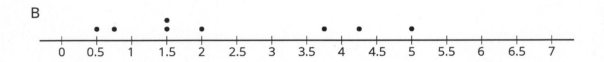

C

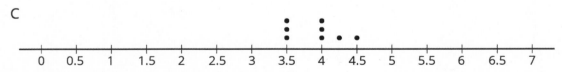

1. One of these data sets has a mean of 5.57 minutes and another has a mean of 3.91.

    a. Which dot plot shows each of these data sets?

    b. Calculate the mean for the data set on the other dot plot.

2. One of these data sets has a mean absolute deviation of 0.30 and another has a MAD of 0.44.

    a. Which dot plot shows each of these data sets?

    b. Calculate the MAD for the other data set.

3. Do you think the three groups are very different or not? Be prepared to explain your reasoning.

4. A fourth album has a mean length of 8 minutes with a mean absolute deviation of 1.2. Is this data set very different from each of the others?

Lesson 11 Summary

Comparing two individuals is fairly straightforward. The question "Which dog is taller?" can be answered by measuring the heights of two dogs and comparing them directly. Comparing two groups can be more challenging. What does it mean for the basketball team to generally be taller than the soccer team?

To compare two groups, we use the distribution of values for the two groups. Most importantly, a measure of center (usually *mean* or *median*) and its associated measure of variability (usually *mean absolute deviation* or *interquartile range)* can help determine the differences between groups.

For example, if the average height of pugs in a dog show is 11 inches, and the average height of the beagles in the dog show is 15 inches, it seems that the beagles are generally taller. On the other hand, if the MAD is 3 inches, it would not be unreasonable to find a beagle that is 11 inches tall or a pug that is 14 inches tall. Therefore the heights of the two dog breeds may not be very different from one another.

Lesson 11 Glossary Terms

- interquartile range (IQR)
- median
- mean
- mean absolute deviation (MAD)

Lesson 11 Practice Problems

1. Compare the weights of the backpacks for the students in these three classes.

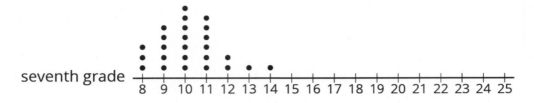

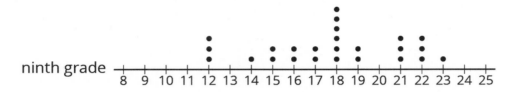

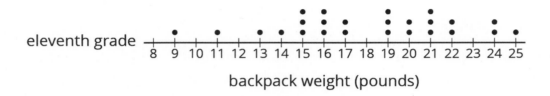

backpack weight (pounds)

2. A bookstore has marked down the price for all the books in a certain series by 15%.

    a. How much is the discount on a book that normally costs $18.00?

    b. After the discount, how much would the book cost?

3. Match each expression in List A with an equivalent expression from List B.

List A:

A. $6(x + 2y) - 2(y - 2x)$

B. $2.5(2x + 4y) - 5(4y - x)$

C. $7.9(5x + 3y) - 4.2(5x + 3y) - 1.7(5x + 3y)$

D. $4(5x - 3y) - 10x + 6y$

E. $5.5(x + y) - 2(x + y) + 6.5(x + y)$

List B:

1. 10(x-y)

2. 10(x+y)

3. 10x+6y

4. 10x-6y

4. Angles C and D are complementary. The ratio of the measure of Angle C to the measure of Angle D is 2 : 3. Find the measure of each angle. Explain or show your reasoning.

Lesson 12: Larger Populations

Let's compare larger groups.

12.1: First Name versus Last Name

Consider the question: In general, do the students at this school have more letters in their first name or last name? How many more letters?

1. What are some ways you might get some data to answer the question?

2. The other day, we compared the heights of people on different teams and the lengths of songs on different albums. What makes this question about first and last names harder to answer than those questions?

12.2: John Jacobjingleheimerschmidt

Continue to consider the question from the warm-up: In general, do the students at this school have more letters in their first name or last name? How many more letters?

1. How many letters are in your first name? In your last name?

2. Do the number of letters in your own first and last names give you enough information to make conclusions about students' names in your entire school? Explain your reasoning.

Grade 7 Mathematics

3. Your teacher will provide you with data from the class. Record the mean number of letters as well as the mean absolute deviation for each data set.

    a. The first names of the students in your class.

    b. The last names of the students in your class.

4. Which mean is larger? By how much? What does this difference tell you about the situation?

5. Do the mean numbers of letters in the first and last names for everyone in your class give you enough information to make conclusions about students' names in your entire school? Explain your reasoning.

12.3: Siblings and Pets

Consider the question: Do people who are the only child *have more pets*?

1. Earlier, we used information about the people in your class to answer a question about the entire school. Would surveying only the people in your class give you enough information to answer this new question? Explain your reasoning.

2. If you had to have an answer to this question by the end of class today, how would you gather data to answer the question?

3. If you could come back tomorrow with your answer to this question, how would you gather data to answer the question?

4. If someone else in the class came back tomorrow with an answer that was different than yours, what would that mean? How would you determine which answer was better?

12.4: Sampling the Population

For each question, identify the **population** and a possible **sample**.

1. What is the mean number of pages for novels that were on the best seller list in the 1990s?

2. What fraction of new cars sold between August 2010 and October 2016 were built in the United States?

3. What is the median income for teachers in North America?

4. What is the average lifespan of Tasmanian devils?

Are you ready for more?

Political parties often use samples to poll people about important issues. One common method is to call people and ask their opinions. In most places, though, they are not allowed to call cell phones. Explain how this restriction might lead to inaccurate samples of the population.

Lesson 12 Summary

A **population** is a set of people or things that we want to study. Here are some examples of populations:

- All people in the world
- All seventh graders at a school
- All apples grown in the U.S.

A **sample** is a subset of a population. Here are some examples of samples from the listed populations:

- The leaders of each country
- The seventh graders who are in band
- The apples in the school cafeteria

When we want to know more about a population but it is not feasible to collect data from everyone in the population, we often collect data from a sample. In the lessons that follow, we will learn more about how to pick a sample that can help answer questions about the entire population.

Lesson 12 Glossary Terms

- sample
- population

Lesson 12 Practice Problems

1. Suppose that you are interested in learning about how much time seventh grade students at your school spend outdoors on a typical school day.

   Select **all** the samples that are a part of the population you are interested in.

   A. The 20 students in a seventh grade math class.
   B. The first 20 students to arrive at school on a particular day.
   C. The seventh grade students participating in a science fair put on by the four middle schools in a school district.
   D. The 10 seventh graders on the school soccer team.
   E. The students on the school debate team.

2. For each sample given, list two possible populations they could belong to.

   a. Sample: The prices for apples at two stores near your house.

   b. Sample: The days of the week the students in your math class ordered food during the past week.

   c. Sample: The daily high temperatures for the capital cities of all 50 U.S. states over the past year.

3. A school's art club holds a bake sale on Fridays to raise money for art supplies. Here are the number of cookies they sold each week in the fall and in the spring:

fall	20	26	25	24	29	20	19	19	24	24
spring	19	27	29	21	25	22	26	21	25	25

a. Find the mean number of cookies sold in the fall and in the spring.

b. The MAD for the fall data is 2.8 cookies. The MAD for the spring data is 2.6 cookies. Express the difference in means as a multiple of the larger MAD.

c. Based on this data, do you think that sales were generally higher in the spring than in the fall?

4. If 6 coins are flipped, find the probability that there is at least 1 heads.

5. A school is selling candles for a fundraiser. They keep 40% of the total sales as their commission, and they pay the rest to the candle company.

price of candle	number of candles sold
small candle: $11	68
medium candle: $18	45
large candle: $25	21

How much money must the school pay to the candle company?

Lesson 13: What Makes a Good Sample?

Let's see what makes a good sample.

13.1: Number Talk: Division by Powers of 10

Find the value of each quotient mentally.

$34,000 \div 10$

$340 \div 100$

$34 \div 10$

$3.4 \div 100$

13.2: Selling Paintings

Your teacher will assign you to work with either means or medians.

1. A young artist has sold 10 paintings. Calculate the measure of center you were assigned for each of these samples:

   a. The first two paintings she sold were for $50 and $350.

   b. At a gallery show, she sold three paintings for $250, $400, and $1,200.

   c. Her oil paintings have sold for $410, $400, and $375.

2. Here are the selling prices for all 10 of her paintings:

$50	$200	$250	$275	$280	$350	$375	$400	$410	$1,200

   Calculate the measure of center you were assigned for all of the selling prices.

Grade 7 Mathematics

3. Compare your answers with your partner. Were the measures of center for any of the samples close to the same measure of center for the population?

13.3: Sampling the Fish Market

m.openup.org/1/7-8-13-3

The price per pound of catfish at a fish market was recorded for 100 weeks.

1. Here are dot plots showing the population and three different samples from that population. What do you notice? What do you wonder?

Population

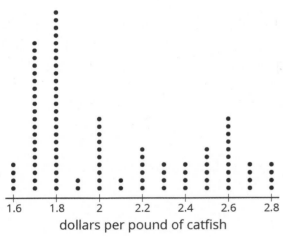

Sample 1

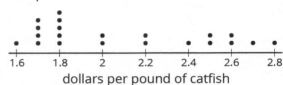

Sample 2

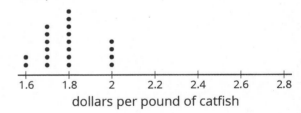

Sample 3

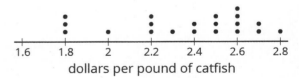

2. If the goal is to have the sample represent the population, which of the samples would work best? Which wouldn't work so well? Explain your reasoning.

Are you ready for more?

When doing a statistical study, it is important to keep the goal of the study in mind. Representative samples give us the best information about the distribution of the population as a whole, but sometimes a representative sample won't work for the goal of a study!

For example, suppose you want to study how discrimination affects people in your town. Surveying a representative sample of people in your town would give information about how the population generally feels, but might miss some smaller groups. Describe a way you might choose a sample of people to address this question.

13.4: Auditing Sales

An online shopping company tracks how many items they sell in different categories during each month for a year. Three different auditors each take samples from that data. Use the samples to draw dot plots of what the population data might look like for the furniture and electronics categories.

Auditor 1's sample
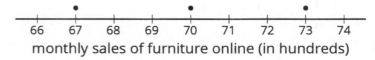

Auditor 2's sample
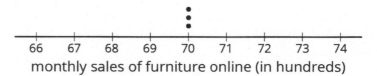

Auditor 3's sample
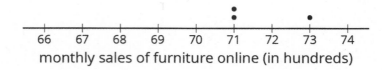

Population
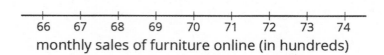

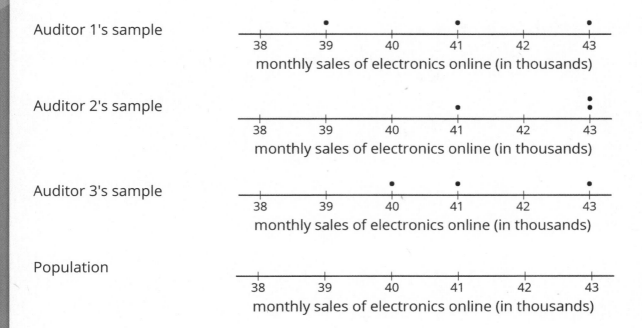

Auditor 1's sample

monthly sales of electronics online (in thousands)

Auditor 2's sample

monthly sales of electronics online (in thousands)

Auditor 3's sample

monthly sales of electronics online (in thousands)

Population

monthly sales of electronics online (in thousands)

Lesson 13 Summary

A sample that is *representative* of a population has a distribution that closely resembles the distribution of the population in shape, center, and spread.

For example, consider the distribution of plant heights, in cm, for a population of plants shown in this dot plot. The mean for this population is 4.9 cm, and the MAD is 2.6 cm.

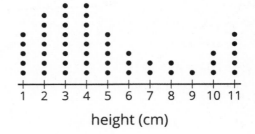

A representative sample of this population should have a larger peak on the left and a smaller one on the right, like this one. The mean for this sample is 4.9 cm, and the MAD is 2.3 cm.

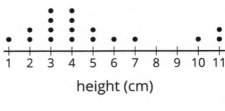

Here is the distribution for another sample from the same population. This sample has a mean of 5.7 cm and a MAD of 1.5 cm. These are both very different from the population, and the distribution has a very different shape, so it is not a representative sample.

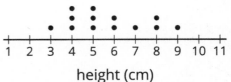

Lesson 13 Practice Problems

1. Suppose that 45% of all of the students at Andre's school brought in a can of food to contribute to a canned food drive. Andre picks a representative sample of 25 students from the school and determine the sample's percentage.

   He expects that the percentage for this sample will be 45%. Do you agree? Explain your thinking.

2. This is a dot plot of the scores on a video game for a population of 50 teenagers.

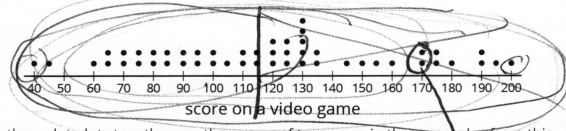

The three dot plots together are the scores of teenagers in three samples from this population. Which of the three samples is most representative of the population? Explain how you know.

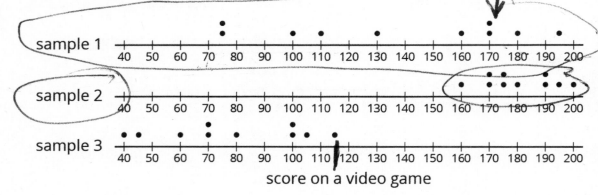

Grade 7
Mathematics

3. This is a dot plot of the number of text messages sent one day for a sample of the students at a local high school. The sample consisted of 30 students and was selected to be representative of the population.

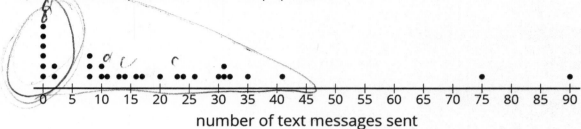

number of text messages sent

   a. What do the five values of 0 in the dot plot represent?

   b. Since this sample is representative of the population, describe what you think a dot plot for the entire population might look like.

4. A doctor suspects you might have a certain strain of flu and wants to test your blood for the presence of markers for this strain of virus. Why would it be good for the doctor to take a sample of your blood rather than use the population?

5. How many different outcomes are in each sample space? Explain your reasoning.

   (You do not need to write out the actual options, just provide the number and your reasoning.)

   a. A letter of the English alphabet is followed by a digit from 0 to 9.

   b. A baseball team's cap is selected from 3 different colors, 2 different clasps, 4 different locations for the team logo. A decision is made to include or not to include reflective piping.

   c. A locker combination like 7-23-11 uses three numbers, each from 1 to 40. Numbers can be used more than once, like 7-23-7.

Lesson 14: Sampling in a Fair Way

Let's explore ways to get representative samples.

14.1: Ages of Moviegoers

A survey was taken at a movie theater to estimate the average age of moviegoers.

Here is a dot plot showing the ages of the first 20 people surveyed.

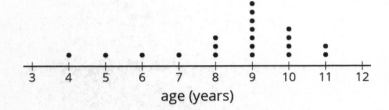

age (years)

1. What questions do you have about the data from survey?

2. What assumptions would you make based on these results?

14.2: Comparing Methods for Selecting Samples

Take turns with your partner reading each option aloud. For each situation, discuss:

- Would the different methods for selecting a sample lead to different conclusions about the population?
- What are the benefits of each method?
- What might each method overlook?
- Which of the methods listed would be the most likely to produce samples that are representative of the population being studied?
- Can you think of a better way to select a sample for this situation?

1. Lin is running in an election to be president of the seventh grade. She wants to predict her chances of winning. She has the following ideas for surveying a sample of the students who will be voting:

   a. Ask everyone on her basketball team who they are voting for.

   b. Ask every third girl waiting in the lunch line who they are voting for.

   c. Ask the first 15 students to arrive at school one morning who they are voting for.

2. A nutritionist wants to collect data on how much caffeine the average American drinks per day. She has the following ideas for how she could obtain a sample:

   a. Ask the first 20 adults who arrive at a grocery store after 10:00 a.m. about the average amount of caffeine they consume each day.

   b. Every 30 minutes, ask the first adult who comes into a coffee shop about the average amount of caffeine they consume each day.

14.3: That's the First Straw

Your teacher will have some students draw straws from a bag.

1. As each straw is taken out and measured, record its length (in inches) in the table.

	straw 1	straw 2	straw 3	straw 4	straw 5
sample 1					
sample 2					

2. Estimate the mean length of all the straws in the bag based on:

   a. the mean of the first sample.

   b. the mean of the second sample.

3. Were your two estimates the same? Did the mean length of all the straws in the bag change in between selecting the two samples? Explain your reasoning.

4. The actual mean length of all of the straws in the bag is about 2.37 inches. How do your estimates compare to this mean length?

5. If you repeated the same process again but you selected a larger sample (such as 10 or 20 straws, instead of just 5), would your estimate be more accurate? Explain your reasoning.

14.4: That's the Last Straw

There were a total of 35 straws in the bag. Suppose we put the straws in order from shortest to longest and then assigned each straw a number from 1 to 35. For each of these methods, decide whether it would be fair way to select a sample of 5 straws. Explain your reasoning.

1. Select the straws numbered 1 through 5.

2. Write the numbers 1 through 35 on pieces of paper that are all the same size. Put the papers into a bag. Without looking, select five papers from the bag. Use the straws with those numbers for your sample.

3. Using the same bag as the previous question, select one paper from the bag. Use the number on that paper to select the first straw for your sample. Then use the next 4 numbers in order to complete your sample. (For example, if you select number 17, then you also use straws 18, 19, 20, and 21 for your sample.)

4. Create a spinner with 35 sections that are all the same size, and number them 1 through 35. Spin the spinner 5 times and use the straws with those numbers for your sample.

Are you ready for more?

Computers accept inputs, follow instructions, and produce outputs, so they cannot produce truly random numbers. If you knew the input, you could predict the output by following the same instructions the computer is following. When truly random numbers are needed, scientists measure natural phenomena such as radioactive decay or temperature variations. Before such measurements were possible, statisticians used random number tables, like this:

```
85 67 95 02 42 61 21 35 15 34 41
85 94 61 72 53 24 15 67 85 94 12
67 88 15 32 42 65 75 98 46 25 13
07 53 60 75 82 34 67 44 20 42 33
99 37 40 33 40 88 90 50 75 22 90
00 03 84 57 91 15 70 08 90 03 02
78 07 16 51 13 89 67 64 54 05 26
62 06 61 43 02 60 73 58 38 53 88
02 50 88 44 37 05 13 54 78 97 30
```

Use this table to select a sample of 5 straws. Pick a starting point at random in the table. If the number is between 01 and 35, include that number straw in your sample. If the number has already been selected, or is not between 01 and 35, ignore it, and move on to the next number.

Lesson 14 Summary

A sample is *selected at random* from a population if it has an equal chance of being selected as every other sample of the same size. For example, if there are 25 students in a class, then we can write each of the students' names on a slip of paper and select 5 papers from a bag to get a sample of 5 students selected at random from the class.

Other methods of selecting a sample from a population are likely to be *biased*. This means that it is less likely that the sample will be representative of the population as a whole. For example, if we select the first 5 students who walk in the door, that will not give us a random sample because students who typically come late are not likely to be selected. A sample that is selected at random may not always be a representative sample, but it is more likely to be representative than using other methods.

It is not always possible to select a sample at random. For example, if we want to know the average length of wild salmon, it is not possible to identify each one individually, select a few at random from the list, and then capture and measure those exact fish. When a sample cannot be selected at random, it is important to try to reduce bias as much as possible when selecting the sample.

Lesson 14 Practice Problems

1. The meat department manager at a grocery store is worried that some of the packages of ground beef that are labeled as having one pound of meat may be under-filled. He decides to take a sample of 5 packages from a shipment containing 100 packages of ground beef. The packages were numbered as they were put in the box, so each one has a different number between 1 and 100.

   Describe how the manager can select a fair sample of 5 packages.

2. Select **all** the reasons why random samples are preferred above other methods of getting a sample.

   A. If you select a random sample, you can determine how many people you want in the sample.
   B. A random sample is always the easiest way to select a sample from a population.
   C. A random sample is likely to give you a sample that is representative of the population.
   D. A random sample is a fair way to select a sample, because each person in the population has an equal chance of being selected.
   E. If you use a random sample, the sample mean will always be the same as the population mean.

3. Jada is using a computer's random number generator to produce 6 random whole numbers between 1 and 100 so she can use a random sample. The computer produces the numbers: 1, 2, 3, 4, 5, and 6. Should she use these numbers or have the computer generate a new set of random numbers? Explain your reasoning.

4. A group of 100 people is divided into 5 groups with 20 people in each. One person's name is chosen, and everyone in their group wins a prize. Noah simulates this situation by writing 100 different names on papers and putting them in a bag, then drawing one out. Kiran suggests there is a way to do it with fewer paper slips. Explain a method that would simulate this situation with fewer than 100 slips of paper.

5. Data collected from a survey of American teenagers aged 13 to 17 was used to estimate that 29% of teens believe in ghosts. This estimate was based on data from 510 American teenagers. What is the population that people carrying out the survey were interested in?

   A. All people in the United States.
   B. The 510 teens that were surveyed.
   C. All American teens who are between the age of 13 and 17.
   D. The 29% of the teens surveyed who said they believe in ghosts.

6. A computer simulates flipping a coin 100 times, then counts the longest string of heads in a row.

trial	most heads in a row
1	8
2	6
3	5
4	11
5	13

Based on these results, estimate the probability that there will be at least 15 heads in a row.

Lesson 15: Estimating Population Measures of Center

Let's use samples to estimate measures of center for the population.

15.1: Describing the Center

Would you use the median or mean to describe the center of each data set? Explain your reasoning.

Heights of 50 basketball players

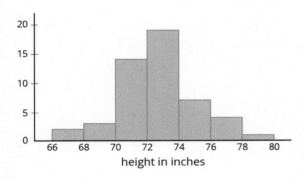

Ages of 30 people at a family dinner party

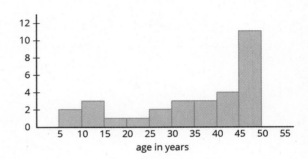

Backpack weights of sixth-grade students

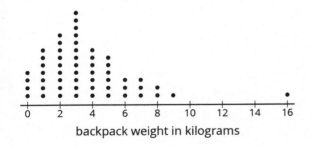

How many books students read over summer break

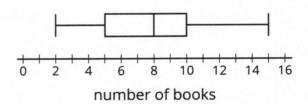

15.2: Three Different TV Shows

Here are the ages (in years) of a random sample of 10 viewers for 3 different television shows. The shows are titled, "Science Experiments YOU Can Do," "Learning to Read," and "Trivia the Game Show."

sample 1	6	6	5	4	8	5	7	8	6	6
sample 2	15	14	12	13	12	10	12	11	10	8
sample 3	43	60	50	36	58	50	73	59	69	51

1. Calculate the mean for *one* of the samples. Make sure each person in your group works with a different sample. Record the answers for all three samples.

2. Which show do you think each sample represents? Explain your reasoning.

15.3: Who's Watching What?

Here are three more samples of viewer ages collected for these same 3 television shows.

sample 4	57	71	5	54	52	13	59	65	10	71
sample 5	15	5	4	5	4	3	25	2	8	3
sample 6	6	11	9	56	1	3	11	10	11	2

1. Calculate the mean for *one* of these samples. Record all three answers.

2. Which show do you think each of these samples represents? Explain your reasoning.

3. For each show, estimate the mean age for all the show's viewers.

4. Calculate the mean absolute deviation for *one* of the shows' samples. Make sure each person in your group works with a different sample. Record all three answers.

	Learning to Read	Science Experiments YOU Can Do	Trivia the Game Show
Which sample number?			
MAD			

5. What do the different values for the MAD tell you about each group?

6. An advertiser has a commercial that appeals to 15- to 16-year-olds. Based on these samples, are any of these shows a good fit for this commercial? Explain or show your reasoning.

15.4: Movie Reviews

A movie rating website has many people rate a new movie on a scale of 0 to 100. Here is a dot plot showing a random sample of 20 of these reviews.

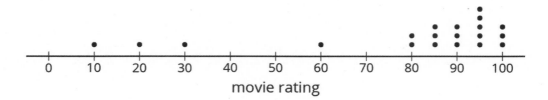

movie rating

1. Would the mean or median be a better measure for the center of this data? Explain your reasoning.

2. Use the sample to estimate the measure of center that you chose for *all* the reviews.

3. For this sample, the mean absolute deviation is 19.6, and the interquartile range is 15. Which of these values is associated with the measure of center that you chose?

4. Movies must have an average rating of 75 or more from all the reviews on the website to be considered for an award. Do you think this movie will be considered for the award? Use the measure of center and measure of variability that you chose to justify your answer.

Are you ready for more?

Estimate typical temperatures in the United States today by looking up current temperatures in several places across the country. Use the data you collect to decide on the appropriate measure of center for the country, and calculate the related measure of variation for your sample.

Lesson 15 Summary

Some populations have greater variability than others. For example, we would expect greater variability in the weights of dogs at a dog park than at a beagle meetup.

Dog park:

Beagle meetup:

Mean weight: 10.1 kg   MAD: 0.8 kg

Mean weight: 12.8 kg   MAD: 2.3 kg

The lower MAD indicates there is less variability in the weights of the beagles. We would expect that the mean weight from a sample that is randomly selected from a group of beagles will provide a more accurate estimate of the mean weight of all the beagles than a sample of the same size from the dogs at the dog park.

In general, a sample of a similar size from a population with *less* variability is *more likely* to have a mean that is close to the population mean.

Lesson 15 Practice Problems

1. A random sample of 15 items were selected.

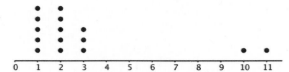

   For this data set, is the mean or median a better measure of center? Explain your reasoning.

2. A video game developer wants to know how long it takes people to finish playing their new game. They surveyed a random sample of 13 players and asked how long it took them (in minutes).

1,235	952	457	1,486	1,759	1,148	548	1,037	1,864	1,245	976	866	1,431

   a. Estimate the median time it will take *all* players to finish this game.

   b. Find the interquartile range for this sample.

3. Han and Priya want to know the mean height of the 30 students in their dance class. They each selected a random sample of 5 students.

   ○ The mean height for Han's sample is 59 inches.
   ○ The mean height for Priya's sample is 61 inches.

   Does it surprise you that the two sample means are different? Are the population means different? Explain your reasoning.

4. Clare and Priya each took a random sample of 25 students at their school.

- Clare asked each student in her sample how much time they spend doing homework each night. The sample mean was 1.2 hours and the MAD was 0.6 hours.
- Priya asked each student in her sample how much time they spend watching TV each night. The sample mean was 2 hours and the MAD was 1.3 hours.

a. At their school, do you think there is more variability in how much time students spend doing homework or watching TV? Explain your reasoning.

b. Clare estimates that the students at her school spend an average of 1.2 hours each night doing homework. Priya estimates that the students at her school spend an average of 2 hours each night watching TV. Which of these two estimates is likely to be closer to the actual mean value for all the students at their school? Explain your reasoning.

Lesson 16: Estimating Population Proportions

Let's estimate population proportions using samples.

16.1: Getting to School

A teacher asked all the students in one class how many minutes it takes them to get to school. Here is a table of their responses:

20	10	15	8	5	15	10	5	20	5	15	10
3	10	18	5	25	5	5	12	10	30	5	10

1. What fraction of the students in this class say:

    a. it takes them 5 minutes to get to school?

    b. it takes them more than 10 minutes to get to school?

2. If the whole school has 720 students, can you use this data to estimate how many of them would say that it takes them more than 10 minutes to get to school?

    Be prepared to explain your reasoning.

16.2: Reaction Times

The track coach at a high school needs a student whose reaction time is less than 0.4 seconds to help out at track meets. All the twelfth graders in the school measured their reaction times. Your teacher will give you a bag of papers that list their results.

1. Work with your partner to select a random sample of 20 reaction times, and record them in the table.

2. What **proportion** of your sample is less than 0.4 seconds?

3. Estimate the proportion of all twelfth graders at this school who have a reaction time of less than 0.4 seconds. Explain your reasoning.

4. There are 120 twelfth graders at this school. Estimate how many of them have a reaction time of less than 0.4 seconds.

5. Suppose another group in your class comes up with a different estimate than yours for the previous question.

   a. What is another estimate that would be *reasonable*?

   b. What is an estimate you would consider *unreasonable*?

16.3: A New Comic Book Hero

Here are the results of a survey of 20 people who read *The Adventures of Super Sam* regarding what special ability they think the new hero should have.

response	what new ability?
1	fly
2	freeze
3	freeze
4	fly
5	fly
6	freeze
7	fly
8	super strength
9	freeze
10	fly

response	what new ability?
11	freeze
12	freeze
13	fly
14	invisibility
15	freeze
16	fly
17	freeze
18	fly
19	super strength
20	freeze

1. What proportion of this sample want the new hero to have the ability to fly?

2. If there are 2,024 dedicated readers of *The Adventures of Super Sam*, estimate the number of readers who want the new hero to fly.

Two other comic books did a similar survey of their readers.

- In a survey of people who read *Beyond Human*, 42 out of 60 people want a new hero to be able to fly.
- In a survey of people who read *Mysterious Planets*, 14 out of 40 people want a new hero to be able to fly.

3. Do you think the proportion of all readers who want a new hero that can fly are nearly the same for the three different comic books? Explain your reasoning.

4. If you were in charge of these three comics, would you give the ability to fly to any of the new heroes? Explain your reasoning using the proportions you calculated.

16.4: Flying to the Shelves

The authors of *The Adventures of Super Sam* chose 50 different random samples of readers. Each sample was of size 20. They looked at the sample proportions who prefer the new hero to fly.

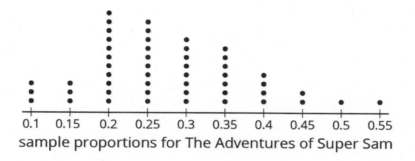

sample proportions for The Adventures of Super Sam

1. What is a good estimate of the proportion of *all* readers who want the new hero to be able to fly?

2. Are most of the sample proportions within 0.1 of your estimate for the population proportion?

3. If the comic book authors give the new hero the ability to fly, will that please most of the readers? Explain your reasoning.

The authors of the other comic book series created similar dot plots.

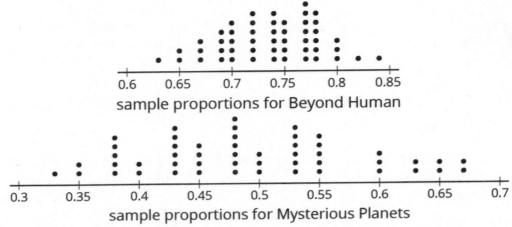

sample proportions for Beyond Human

sample proportions for Mysterious Planets

1. For each of these series, estimate the proportion of all readers who want the new hero to fly.

    a. *Beyond Human*:

    b. *Mysterious Planets*:

2. Should the authors of either of these series give their new hero the ability to fly?

3. Why might it be more difficult for the authors of *Mysterious Planets* to make the decision than the authors of the other series?

Are you ready for more?

Draw an example of a dot plot with at least 20 dots that represent the sample proportions for different random samples that would indicate that the population proportion is above 0.6, but there is a lot of uncertainty about that estimate.

Lesson 16 Summary

Sometimes a data set consists of information that fits into specific categories. For example, we could survey students about whether they have a pet cat or dog. The categories for these data would be {neither, dog only, cat only, both}. Suppose we surveyed 10 students. Here is a table showing possible results:

option	number of responses
neither dog nor cat	2
dog only	4
cat only	1
both dog and cat	3

In this sample, 3 of the students said they have both a dog and a cat. We can say that the **proportion** of these students who have a both a dog and a cat is $\frac{3}{10}$ or 0.3. If this sample is representative of all 720 students at the school, we can predict that about $\frac{3}{10}$ of 720, or about 216 students at the school have both a dog and a cat.

In general, a proportion is a number from 0 to 1 that represents the fraction of the data that belongs to a given category.

Lesson 16 Glossary Terms

- proportion

Lesson 16 Practice Problems

1. Tyler wonders what proportion of students at his school would dye their hair blue if their parents would let them. He surveyed a random sample of 10 students at his school, and 2 of them said they would. Kiran didn't think Tyler's estimate was very accurate, so he surveyed a random sample of 100 students, and 17 of them said that they would.

    a. Based on Tyler's sample, estimate what proportion of the students would dye their hair blue.

    b. Based on Kiran's sample, estimate what proportion of the students would dye their hair blue.

    c. Whose estimate is more accurate? Explain how you know.

2. Han surveys a random sample of students about their favorite pasta dish served by the cafeteria and makes a bar graph of the results.

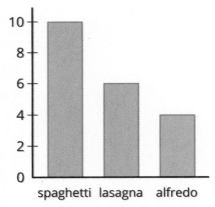

Estimate the proportion of the school who likes lasagna as their favorite pasta dish.

Grade 7 Mathematics | iM

3. Elena wants to know what proportion of people have cats as pets. Describe a process that she could use to estimate an answer to her question.

4. The science teacher gives daily homework. For a random sample of days throughout the year, the median number of problems is 5 and the IQR is 2. The Spanish teacher also gives daily homework. For a random sample of days throughout the year, the median number of problems is 10 and the IQR is 1. If you estimate the median number of science homework problems to be 5 and the median number of Spanish problems to be 10, which is more likely to be accurate? Explain your reasoning.

5. Diego wants to survey a sample of students at his school to learn about the percentage of students who are satisfied with the food in the cafeteria. He decides to go to the cafeteria on a Monday and ask the first 25 students who purchase a lunch at the cafeteria if they are satisfied with the food.

   Do you think that this is a good way for Diego to select his sample? Explain your reasoning.

Lesson 17: More about Sampling Variability

Let's compare samples from the same population.

17.1: Average Reactions

The other day, you worked with the reaction times of twelfth graders to see if they were fast enough to help out at the track meet. Look back at the sample you collected.

1. Calculate the mean reaction time for your sample.

2. Did you and your partner get the same sample mean? Explain why or why not.

17.2: Reaction Population

Your teacher will display a blank dot plot.

1. Plot your sample mean from the previous activity on your teacher's dot plot.

2. What do you notice about the distribution of the sample means from the class?

    a. Where is the center?

    b. Is there a lot of variability?

    c. Is it approximately symmetric?

3. The population mean is 0.442 seconds. How does this value compare to the sample means from the class?

Pause here so your teacher can display a dot plot of the population of reaction times.

4. What do you notice about the distribution of the population?

    a. Where is the center?

    b. Is there a lot of variability?

    c. Is it approximately symmetric?

5. Compare the two displayed dot plots.

6. Based on the distribution of sample means from the class, do you think the mean of a random sample of 20 items is likely to be:

    a. within 0.01 seconds of the actual population mean?

    b. within 0.1 seconds of the actual population mean?

    Explain or show your reasoning.

17.3: How Much Do You Trust the Answer?

The other day you worked with 2 different samples of viewers from each of 3 different television shows. Each sample included 10 viewers. Here are the mean ages for 100 different samples of viewers from each show.

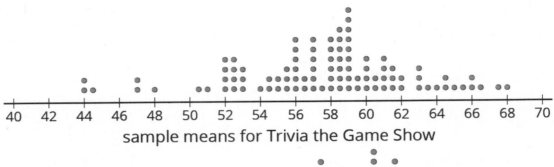

sample means for Trivia the Game Show

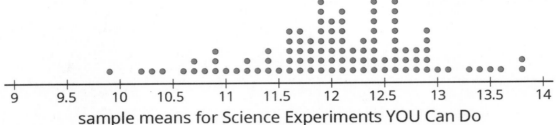

sample means for Science Experiments YOU Can Do

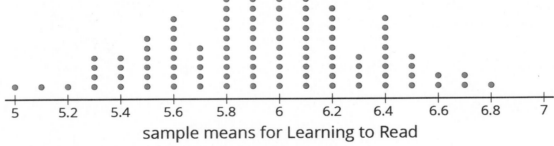

sample means for Learning to Read

1. For each show, use the dot plot to estimate the *population* mean.

    a. Trivia the Game Show

    b. Science Experiments YOU Can Do

    c. Learning to Read

2. For each show, are most of the sample means within 1 year of your estimated population mean?

3. Suppose you take a new random sample of 10 viewers for each of the 3 shows. Which show do you expect to have the new sample mean closest to the population mean? Explain or show your reasoning.

Are you ready for more?

Market research shows that advertisements for retirement plans appeal to people between the ages of 40 and 55. Younger people are usually not interested and older people often already have a plan. Is it a good idea to advertise retirement plans during any of these three shows? Explain your reasoning.

Lesson 17 Summary

This dot plot shows the weights, in grams, of 18 cookies. The triangle indicates the mean weight, which is 11.6 grams.

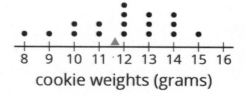

cookie weights (grams)

This dot plot shows the *means* of 20 samples of 5 cookies, selected at random. Again, the triangle shows the mean for the *population* of cookies. Notice that most of the sample means are fairly close to the mean of the entire population.

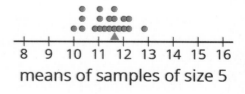

means of samples of size 5

This dot plot shows the means of 20 samples of 10 cookies, selected at random. Notice that the means for these samples are even closer to the mean for the entire population.

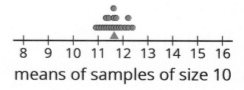

means of samples of size 10

In general, as the sample size gets bigger, the mean of a sample is more likely to be closer to the mean of the population.

Lesson 17 Practice Problems

1. One thousand baseball fans were asked how far they would be willing to travel to watch a professional baseball game. From this population, 100 different samples of size 40 were selected. Here is a dot plot showing the mean of each sample.

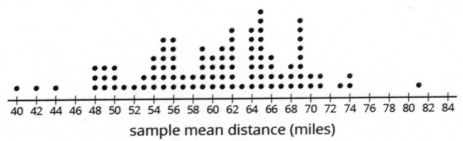

sample mean distance (miles)

Based on the distribution of sample means, what do you think is a reasonable estimate for the mean of the population?

2. Last night, everyone at the school music concert wrote their age on a slip of paper and placed it in a box. Today, each of the students in a math class selected a random sample of size 10 from the box of papers. Here is a dot plot showing their sample means, rounded to the nearest year.

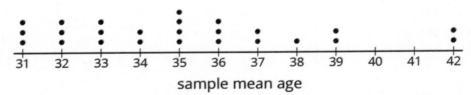

sample mean age

   a. Does the number of dots on the dot plot tell you how many people were at the concert or how many students are in the math class?

   b. The mean age for the population was 35 years. If Elena picks a new sample of size 10 from this population, should she expect her sample mean to be within 1 year of the population mean? Explain your reasoning.

   c. What could Elena do to select a random sample that is more likely to have a sample mean within 1 year of the population mean?

Grade 7
Mathematics

3. A random sample of people were asked which hand they preferred to write with.

   l means they prefer to use their left hand.

   r means they prefer to use their right hand.

| l | r | r | r | r | r | r | r | r | r | l | r | r | r | r |

   Based on this sample, estimate the proportion of the population that prefers to write with their left hand.

4. Andre would like to estimate the mean number of books that the students at his school read over the summer break. He has a list of the names of all the students at the school, but he doesn't have time to ask every student how many books they read.

   What should Andre do to estimate the mean number of books?

5. A hockey team has a 75% chance of winning against the opposing team in each game of a playoff series. To win the series, the team must be the first to win 4 games.

   a. Design a simulation for this event.

   b. What counts as a successful outcome in your simulation?

   c. Estimate the probability using your simulation.

Lesson 18: Comparing Populations Using Samples

Let's compare different populations using samples.

18.1: Same Mean? Same MAD?

Without calculating, tell whether each pair of data sets have the same mean and whether they have the same mean absolute deviation.

set A	1	3	3	5	6	8	10	14

set B	21	23	23	25	26	28	30	34

set X	1	2	3	4	5

set Y	1	2	3	4	5	6

set P	47	53	58	62

set Q	37	43	68	72

18.2: With a Heavy Load

Consider the question: Do tenth-grade students' backpacks generally weigh more than seventh-grade students' backpacks?

Here are dot plots showing the weights of backpacks for a random sample of students from these two grades:

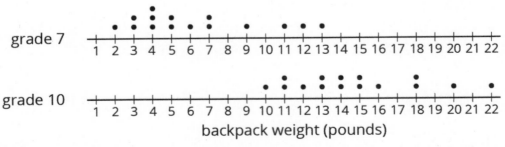

backpack weight (pounds)

1. Did any seventh-grade backpacks in this sample weigh more than a tenth-grade backpack?

Grade 7 Mathematics

2. The mean weight of this sample of seventh-grade backpacks is 6.3 pounds. Do you think the mean weight of backpacks for *all* seventh-grade students is exactly 6.3 pounds?

3. The mean weight of this sample of tenth-grade backpacks is 14.8 pounds. Do you think there is a meaningful difference between the weight of all seventh-grade and tenth-grade students' backpacks? Explain or show your reasoning.

18.3: Do They Carry More?

Here are 10 more random samples of seventh-grade students' backpack weights.

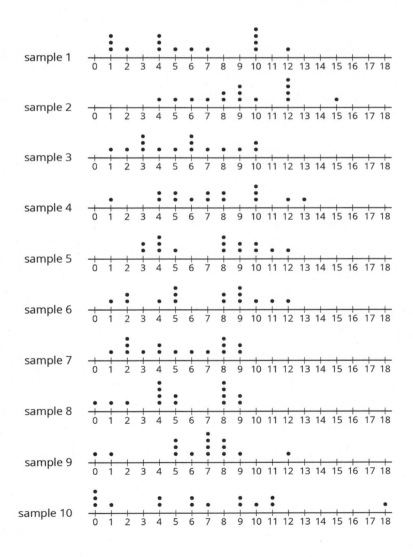

sample number	mean weight (pounds)
1	5.8
2	9.2
3	5.5
4	7.3
5	7.2
6	6.6
7	5.2
8	5.2
9	6.3
10	6.4

1. a. Which sample has the highest mean weight?

   b. Which sample has the lowest mean weight?

   c. What is the difference between these two sample means?

2. All of the samples have a mean absolute deviation of about 2.8 pounds. Express the difference between these two sample means as a multiple of the MAD.

3. Are these samples very different? Explain or show your reasoning.

Remember our sample of tenth-grade students' backpacks had a mean weight of 14.8 pounds. The MAD for this sample is 2.7 pounds. Your teacher will assign you one of the samples of seventh-grade students' backpacks to use.

4. a. What is the difference between the sample means for the the tenth-grade students' backpacks and the seventh-grade students' backpacks?

   b. Express the difference between these two sample means as a multiple of the larger of the MADs.

5. Do you think there is a meaningful difference between the weights of all seventh-grade and tenth-grade students' backpacks? Explain or show your reasoning.

18.4: Steel from Different Regions

When anthropologists find steel artifacts, they can test the amount of carbon in the steel to learn about the people that made the artifacts. Here are some box plots showing the percentage of carbon in samples of steel that were found in two different regions:

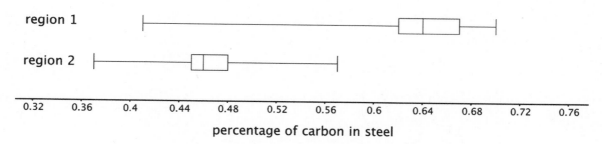

percentage of carbon in steel

1. Was there any steel found in region 1 that had:

    a. *more* carbon than some of the steel found in region 2?

    b. *less* carbon than some of the steel found in region 2?

2. Do you think there is a meaningful difference between all the steel artifacts found in regions 1 and 2?

3. Which sample has a distribution that is *not* approximately symmetric?

	sample median (%)	IQR (%)
region 1	0.64	0.05
region 2	0.47	0.03

4. What is the difference between the sample medians for these two regions?

5. Express the difference between these two sample medians as a multiple of the larger interquartile range.

6. The anthropologists who conducted the study concluded that there was a meaningful difference between the steel from these regions. Do you agree? Explain or show your reasoning.

Lesson 18 Summary

Sometimes we want to compare two different populations. For example, is there a meaningful difference between the weights of pugs and beagles? Here are histograms showing the weights for a sample of dogs from each of these breeds:

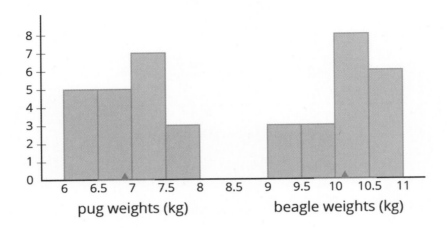

pug weights (kg)   beagle weights (kg)

The red triangles show the mean weight of each sample, 6.9 kg for the pugs and 10.1 kg for the beagles. The red lines show the weights that are within 1 MAD of the mean. We can think of these as "typical" weights for the breed. These typical weights do not overlap. In fact, the distance between the means is $10.1 - 6.9$ or 3.2 kg, over 6 times the larger MAD! So we can say there *is* a meaningful difference between the weights of pugs and beagles.

Is there a meaningful difference between the weights of male pugs and female pugs? Here are box plots showing the weights for a sample of male and female pugs:

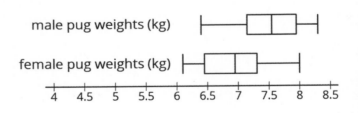

We can see that the medians are different, but the weights between the first and third quartiles overlap. Based on these samples, we would say there is *not* a meaningful difference between the weights of male pugs and female pugs.

In general, if the measures of center for two samples are at least two measures of variability apart, we say the difference in the measures of center is meaningful. Visually, this means the range of typical values does not overlap. If they are closer, then we don't consider the difference to be meaningful.

Grade 7 Mathematics

Lesson 18 Practice Problems

1. Lin wants to know if students in elementary school generally spend more time playing outdoors than students in middle school. She selects a random sample of size 20 from each population of students and asks them how many hours they played outdoors last week. Suppose that the MAD for each of her samples is about 3 hours.

   Select **all** the pairs of sample means for which Lin could conclude that there is a meaningful difference between the two populations.

   A. Elementary school: 12 hours, Middle school: 10 hours
   B. Elementary school: 14 hours, Middle school: 9 hours
   C. Elementary school: 13 hours, Middle school: 6 hours
   D. Elementary school: 13 hours, Middle school: 10 hours
   E. Elementary school: 7 hours, Middle school: 15 hours

2. These two box plots show the distances of a standing jump, in inches, for a random sample of 10-year-olds and a random sample of 15-year-olds.

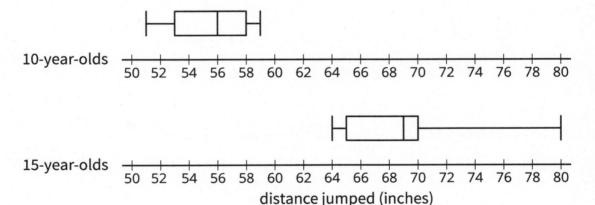

   Is there is a meaningful difference in median distance for the two populations? Explain how you know.

3. The median income for a sample of people from Chicago is about $60,000 and for a sample of people from Kansas City is about $46,000, but researchers have determined there is not a meaningful difference in the medians. Explain why the researchers might be correct.

4. A farmer grows 5,000 pumpkins each year. The pumpkins are priced according to their weight, so the farmer would like to estimate the mean weight of the pumpkins he has grown this year. He randomly selects 8 pumpkins and weighs them. Here are the weights (in pounds) of these pumpkins:

weight (pounds)	2.9	6.8	7.3	7.7	8.9	10.6	12.3	15.3

a. Estimate the mean weight of the pumpkins that the farmer has grown.

This dot plot shows the mean weight of 100 samples of eight pumpkins, similar to the one above.

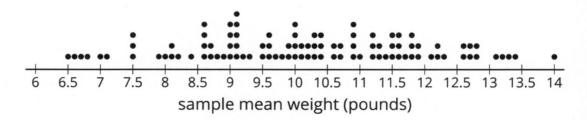

b. What appears to be the mean weight of the 5,000 pumpkins?

c. What does the dot plot of the sample means suggest about how accurate an estimate based on a single sample of 8 pumpkins might be?

d. What do you think the farmer might do to get a more accurate estimate of the population mean?

Lesson 19: Comparing Populations With Friends

Let's ask important questions to compare groups.

19.1: Features of Graphic Representations

Dot plots, histograms, and box plots are different ways to represent a data set graphically.

Which of those displays would be the easiest to use to find each feature of the data?

1. the mean

2. the median

3. the mean absolute deviation

4. the interquartile range

5. the symmetry

19.2: Info Gap: Comparing Populations

Your teacher will give you either a problem card or a data card. Do not show or read your card to your partner.

If your teacher gives you the *problem card*:

1. Silently read your card, and think about what information you need to answer the question.

2. Ask your partner for the specific information that you need.

3. Explain to your partner how you are using the information to solve the problem.

4. Solve the problem, and explain your reasoning to your partner.

If your teacher gives you the *data card*:

1. Silently read the information on your card.

2. Ask your partner, "What specific information do you need?" Wait for your partner to *ask* for information. *Only* give information that is on your card. (Do not figure out anything for your partner!)

3. Before telling your partner the information, ask "Why do you need that information?"

4. After your partner solves the problem, ask them to explain their reasoning, and listen to their explanation.

Pause here so your teacher can review your work. Ask your teacher for a new set of cards and repeat the activity, trading roles with your partner.

Are you ready for more?

Is there a meaningful difference between top sports performance in two different decades? Choose a variable from your favorite sport (for example, home runs in baseball, kills in volleyball, aces in tennis, saves in soccer, etc.) and compare the leaders for each year of two different decades. Is the performance in one decade meaningfully different from the other?

19.3: Comparing to Known Characteristics

1. A college graduate is considering two different companies to apply to for a job. Acme Corp lists this sample of salaries on their website:

$45,000	$55,000	$140,000	$70,000	$60,000	$50,000

   What typical salary would Summit Systems need to have to be meaningfully different from Acme Corp? Explain your reasoning.

2. A factory manager is wondering whether they should upgrade their equipment. The manager keeps track of how many faulty products are created each day for a week.

6	7	8	6	7	5	7

   The new equipment guarantees an average of 4 or fewer faulty products per day. Is there a meaningful difference between the new and old equipment? Explain your reasoning.

Lesson 19 Summary

When using samples to comparing two populations, there are a lot of factors to consider.

- Are the samples representative of their populations? If the sample is biased, then it may not have the same center and variability as the population.
- Which characteristic of the populations makes sense to compare—the mean, the median, or a proportion?
- How variable is the data? If the data is very spread out, it can be more difficult to make conclusions with certainty.

Knowing the correct questions to ask when trying to compare groups is important to correctly interpret the results.

Lesson 19 Practice Problems

1. An agent at an advertising agency asks a random sample of people how many episodes of a TV show they watch each day. The results are shown in the dot plot.

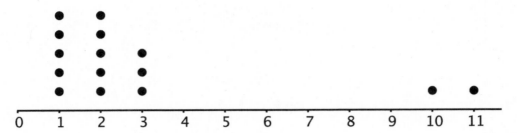

The agency currently advertises on a different show, but wants to change to this one as long as the typical number of episodes is not meaningfully less.

   a. What measure of center and measure of variation would the agent need to find for their current show to determine if there is a meaningful difference? Explain your reasoning.

   b. What are the values for these same characteristics for the data in the dot plot?

   c. What numbers for these characteristics would be meaningfully different if the measure of variability for the current show is similar? Explain your reasoning.

2. Jada wants to know if there is a meaningful difference in the mean number of friends on social media for teens and adults. She looks at the friend count for the 10 most popular of her friends and the friend count for 10 of her parents' friends. She then computes the mean and MAD of each sample and determines there is a meaningful difference. Jada's dad later tells her that he thinks she has not come to the right conclusion. Jada checks her calculations and everything is right. Do you agree with her dad? Explain your reasoning.

3. The mean weight for a sample of a certain kind of ring made from platinum is 8.21 grams. The mean weight for a sample of a certain kind of ring made from gold is 8.61 grams. Is there a meaningful difference in the weights of the two types of rings? Explain your reasoning.

4. The lengths in feet of a random sample of 20 male and 20 female humpback whales were measured and used to create the box plot.

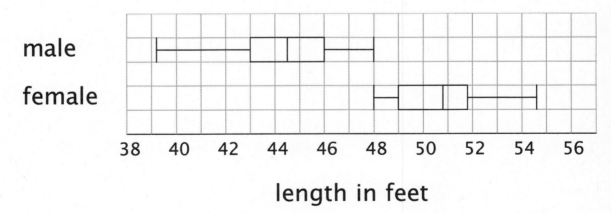

Estimate the median lengths of male and female humpback whales based on these samples.

Lesson 20: Memory Test

Let's put it all together.

20.1: Collecting a Sample

You teacher will give you a paper that lists a data set with 100 numbers in it. Explain whether each method of obtaining a sample of size 20 would produce a random sample.

Option 1: A spinner has 10 equal sections on it. Spin once to get the row number and again to get the column number for each member of your sample. Repeat this 20 times.

Option 2: Since the data looks random already, use the first two rows.

Option 3: Cut up the data and put them into a bag. Shake the bag to mix up the papers, and take out 20 values.

Option 4: Close your eyes and point to one of the numbers to use as your first value in your sample. Then, keep moving one square from where your finger is to get a path of 20 values for your sample.

Grade 7
Mathematics

20.2: Sample Probabilities

Continue working with the data set your teacher gave you in the previous activity. The data marked with a star all came from students at Springfield Middle School.

1. When you select the first value for your random sample, what is the probability that it will be a value that came from a student at Springfield Middle School?

2. What proportion of your entire sample would you expect to be from Springfield Middle School?

3. If you take a random sample of size 10, how many scores would you expect to be from Springfield Middle School?

4. Select a random sample of size 10.

5. Did your random sample have the expected number of scores from Springfield Middle School?

20.3: Estimating a Measure of Center for the Population

1. Decide which measure of center makes the most sense to use based on the distribution of your sample. Discuss your thinking with your partner. If you disagree, work to reach an agreement.

2. Estimate this measure of center for your population based on your sample.

3. Calculate the measure of variability for your sample that goes with the measure of center that you found.

20.4: Comparing Populations

Using only the values you computed in the previous two activities, compare your sample to your partner's.

Is it reasonable to conclude that the measures of center for each of your populations are meaningfully different? Explain or show your reasoning.

My Reflections

Lesson 1: Mystery Bags

- I can get an idea for the likelihood of an event by using results from previous experiments.

Lesson 2: Chance Experiments

- I can describe the likelihood of events using the words impossible, unlikely, equally likely as not, likely, or certain.
- I can tell which event is more likely when the chances of different events are expressed as fractions, decimals, or percentages.

Lesson 3: What Are Probabilities?

- I can write out the sample space for a simple chance experiment.
- I can use the sample space to calculate the probability of an event when all outcomes are equally likely.

Lesson 4: Estimating Probabilities Through Repeated Experiments

- I can explain whether certain results from repeated experiments would be surprising or not.
- I can estimate the probability of an event based on the results from repeating an experiment.

Lesson 5: More Estimating Probabilities

- I can explain why results from repeating an experiment may not exactly match the expected probability for an event.
- I can calculate the probability of an event when the outcomes in the sample space are not equally likely.

Lesson 6: Estimating Probabilities Using Simulation

- I can simulate a real-world situation using a simple experiment that reflects the probability of the actual event.

Lesson 7: Simulating Multi-step Experiments

- I can use a simulation to estimate the probability of a multi-step event.

Lesson 8: Keeping Track of All Possible Outcomes

- I can write out the sample space for a multi-step experiment, using a list, table, or tree diagram.

Lesson 9: Multi-step Experiments

- I can use the sample space to calculate the probability of an event in a multi-step experiment.

Lesson 10: Designing Simulations

- I can design a simulation to estimate the probability of a multi-step real-world situation.

Lesson 11: Comparing Groups

- I can calculate the difference between two means as a multiple of the mean absolute deviation.
- When looking at a pair of dot plots, I can determine whether the distributions are very different or have a lot of overlap.

Lesson 12: Larger Populations

- When I read or hear a statistical question, I can name the population of interest and give an example of a sample for that population.
- I can explain why it may be useful to gather data on a sample of a population.

Lesson 13: What Makes a Good Sample?

- I remember that when a distribution is not symmetric, the median is a better estimate of a typical value than the mean.
- I can determine whether a sample is representative of a population by considering the shape, center, and spread of each of them.
- I know that some samples may represent the population better than others.

Lesson 14: Sampling in a Fair Way

- I can describe ways to get a random sample from a population.
- I know that selecting a sample at random is usually a good way to get a representative sample.

Lesson 15: Estimating Population Measures of Center

- I can estimate the mean or median of a population based on a sample of the population.
- I can consider the variability of a sample to get an idea for how accurate my estimate is.

Lesson 16: Estimating Population Proportions

- I can estimate the proportion of population data that are in a certain category based on a sample.

Lesson 17: More about Sampling Variability

- I can use the means from many samples to judge how accurate an estimate for the population mean is.
- I know that as the sample size gets bigger, the sample mean is more likely to be close to the population mean.

Lesson 18: Comparing Populations Using Samples

- I can calculate the difference between two medians as a multiple of the interquartile range.
- I can determine whether there is a meaningful difference between two populations based on a sample from each population.

Lesson 19: Comparing Populations With Friends

- I can decide what information I need to know to be able to compare two populations based on a sample from each.

Lesson 20: Memory Test

- I can compare two groups by taking a random sample, calculating important measures, and determining whether the populations are meaningfully different.

Glossary

adjacent angles

Two angles are adjacent if they share a side and a vertex, and they don't overlap.

area of a circle

The area of a circle whose radius is r units is πr^2 square units.

A circle has radius 3 inches. Its area is $\pi 3^2 = 9\pi$ square inches, which is approximately 28.3 square inches.

chance experiment

A chance experiment is something you can do over and over again and you don't necessarily know what is going to happen each time. For example, tossing a coin is a chance experiment which could result in heads or tails.

circle

A circle of radius r with center O is the set of all points that are a distance r units from O.

To draw a circle of radius 3 and center O, use a compass to draw all the points at a distance 3 from O.

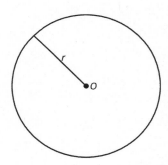

circumference

The circumference of a circle is the distance around the circle. If you imagine the circle as a piece of string, it is the length of the string. If the circle has radius r then the circumference is $2\pi r$.

The circumference of a circle of radius 3 is $2 \cdot \pi \cdot 3 = 6\pi$, which is about 18.85.

complementary

Two angles are complementary to each other if their measures add up to 90°. The two acute angles in a right triangle are complementary to each other.

The complementary angle to 15° is 75°.

constant of proportionality
See proportional relationship.

cross section
A cross section is the two-dimensional figure that is exposed by slicing a three-dimensional object.

diameter
A line segment that has endpoints on a circle and passes through the center is called a diameter of the circle. The length of this segment is also called the diameter.

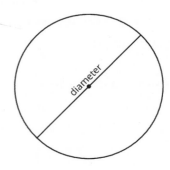

equivalent ratios
Two ratios $a : b$ and $c : d$ are equivalent ratios if there is a number s that you can multiply both a and b by to get c and d (respectively). In other words, $a \cdot s = c$ and $b \cdot s = d$.

$8 : 6$ is equivalent to $4 : 3$ because you can multiply the numbers in the first ratio by $\frac{1}{2}$ to get the numbers in the second ratio.

event
An event is a set of possible outcomes of a chance experiment. It could be just a single outcome, like heads when you toss a coin, or it could be a set of outcomes. For example, when you perform the chance experiment of tossing a coin twice, then "at least one head" is an event that includes the outcomes heads-tails, tails-heads, and heads-heads.

interquartile range (IQR)
The interquartile range of a data set is a measure of spread of its distribution. It is the difference between the third quartile (Q3) and the first quartile (Q1).

12	19	20	21	22	33	34	35	40	40	49
		Q1			Q2			Q3		

The interquartile range is Q3 − Q1 = 40 − 20 = 20.

mean

The mean, or average, of a data set is the value you get by adding up all of the values in the set and dividing by the number of values in the set.

mean absolute deviation (MAD)

The mean absolute deviation measures the spread in a distribution. It is the mean of the distances of the data points from the mean of the distribution. (It is called mean absolute deviation because the distance of a data point from the mean is the absolute value of its deviation from the mean.)

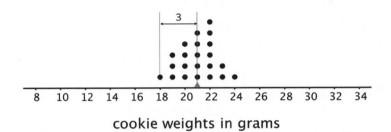

cookie weights in grams

weight in grams	18	19	19	19	20	20	20	20	21	21	21	21	21	22	22	22	22	22	22	23	23	24
distance from mean	3	2	2	2	1	1	1	1	0	0	0	0	0	1	1	1	1	1	1	2	2	3

The dot plot shows a distribution of cookie weights. The data point on the left is a distance of 3 from the mean of the distribution. The second row of the table shows all the distances from the mean. The mean absolute deviation is the mean of the numbers in the second row, which is 1.2.

measurement error

Measurement error is the positive difference between a measurement of a quantity and the actual quantity. It is often expressed as a percentage of the actual value. For example, if we get 6 cm when we measure a line that is actually 6.2 cm long, then the measurement error is 0.2 cm and the percent error is 3.2%, because $0.2 \div 6.2 = 0.032$.

median

The median of a data set is the middle value when the data values are listed in order. If the number of values is even, it is the mean of the two middle values.

origin

In the coordinate plane, the origin is the point $(0, 0)$.

outcome

An outcome of a chance experiment is one of the things that can happen when you do the experiment. For example, the possible outcomes of tossing a coin are heads and tails.

percent error

The difference between the correct value and the incorrect value, expressed as a percentage of the correct value.

The milk carton is supposed to contain 16 fluid ounces but it only contains 15 fluid ounces. The percent error is 6.25% because the error is 1 oz and 1 is 6.25% of 16.

percentage decrease

Given an initial amount, and a final amount which is smaller than the initial amount, the percentage decrease is the difference (initial amount minus final amount) expressed as a percentage of the initial amount.

The bank balance was $200 on Monday and $195 on Tuesday. The percent decrease in the balance from Monday to Tuesday was 2.5%, because 195 is 5 less than 200, and 5 is 2.5% of 200. We can write this as an equation: $195 = 200 - 5 = 200 - 0.025 \cdot 200$.

percentage increase

Given an initial amount, and a final amount which is larger than the initial amount, the percentage increase is the difference (final amount minus initial amount) expressed as a percentage of the initial amount.

The bank balance was $230 on Monday and $253 on Tuesday. The percent increase in the balance from Monday to Tuesday was 10%, because 253 is 23 more than 230, and 23 is 10% of 230. We can write this as an equation: $253 = 230 + 23 = 230 + 0.1 \cdot 230$.

pi (π)

The Greek letter π (pronounced "pie") stands for the number that is the constant of proportionality between the circumference of a circle and its diameter. If d is the diameter and C is the circumference, then $C = \pi d$.

population

A population is a set of people or things that we want to study.

probability

The probability of an event is a number that measures how likely the event is to occur. It can be 0, 1, or any number in between. It is 0 if the event will never occur and 1 if the event always occurs. If an event occurs half the time in the long run then its probability is 0.5.

proportion

For a set of data, a proportion is a number from 0 to 1 that represents the fraction of the data that belongs to a given category.

proportional relationship

If there is a positive constant k so that the quantities x and y are related by the equation $y = kx$, then we say that y and x are in a proportional relationship, and that y is proportional to x. The constant k is called the constant of proportionality.

If a train is moving at a constant speed of 300 kilometers per hour, then the distance it has traveled, d, in kilometers, is proportional to the time, t, in hours, since it started. An equation for the relationship is $d = 300t$ and the constant of proportionality is 300.

radius

The distance from the center of a circle to any point on the circle. Also the corresponding line segment from the center to a point on the circle.

random

If all the outcomes of a chance experiment are equally likely, then we say the outcomes are random, or that they happen at random.

repeating decimal

A repeating decimal is an infinite decimal expansion that eventually repeats the same sequence of digits over and over again. The repeated sequence is indicated by a line above it.

The decimal expansion for $\frac{1}{3}$ is the repeating decimal $0.333\ldots$ or $0.\overline{3}$. The decimal expansion for $\frac{25}{22}$ is $1.13636363\cdots = 1.1\overline{363}$.

right angle

When you divide a straight angle into two equal angles, each of the two angles is a right angle. For example, the four corners of a square are right angles.

sample

A sample is a subset of a population.

sample space

The sample space for a chance experiment is the list of all possible outcomes of the experiment. For example, the sample space for tossing a coin twice is heads-heads, heads-tails, tails-heads, and tails-tails.

scale drawing

A scale drawing of an object is a drawing in which all lengths in the drawing correspond to lengths in the object by the same scale. The scale tells you how the lengths correspond; for example, a scale of "1 inch to 2 feet" means that 1 inch in the drawing represents 2 feet in the object.

scaled copy

A scaled copy of a figure is a figure in which every length in the original figure is increased or decreased by the same scale factor. For example, if you draw copy of a figure in which every length is magnified by 2, then you have a scaled copy with a scale factor of 2.

straight angle

If the two rays that make an angle form a straight line, we call the angle a straight angle.

For example, angle ABC is a straight angle.

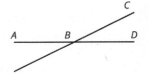

supplementary

Two angles are supplementary to each other if their measures add up to 180°.

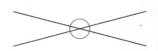

For example, angle ABC is supplementary to angle CBD, because they add up to a straight angle, which has measure 180°.

vertical angles

A pair of vertical angles is a pair of angles that are across from each other at the point where two lines intersect. There are two pairs of vertical angles.